Young Mister Big

The Story
of

Charles Thompson Harvey

the
Young Traveling Salesman Who
Built the World's Mightiest Canal

by
WILLIAM RATIGAN

Author of
SOO CANAL!

WM. B. EERDMANS PUBLISHING CO.
Grand Rapids   1955   Michigan

PRINTED IN THE UNITED STATES OF AMERICA

LIBRARY DEVELOPMENT
PROGRAM

Young Mister Big

The Story of
Charles Thompson Harvey

Tell us now a tale of wonder,

Tell us of some strange adventure....

Longfellow's HIAWATHA

For my Father

B. J. RATIGAN

*Who became a Great Lakes seaman
when a boy of twelve*

CONTENTS

1

Gunfighter Eyes

"Charles!" he heard his mother call sharply from the kitchen of the Presbyterian parsonage in Colchester, Connecticut. "Charles Harvey! You march straight into this house for supper and stop that foolishness out back there!"

The boy, sturdier than average for his twelve years, stopped working on his project beside the spring-fed rivulet that bustled through the woods. But, as he went toward the house, he threw glances behind with his steel-gray eyes, the kind the frontier West would call *gunfighter eyes*.

At the backyard pump, he washed his mud-caked hands, pulled a sliver from his palm, and combed his shock of blond hair with hasty fingers. He arrived at the table with cheeks scrubbed shiny as polished apples, sliding into his chair with a mumbled apology for being late again. "You see, Father, I'm working on a new idea," he began.

The Reverend Joseph Harvey, a direct descendant of the Puritan Governor Bradford of Plymouth Colony, frowned his son to silence, and said Grace. Then Mrs. Harvey, granddaughter of the Continental Colonel who had raised the first regiment in New England that joined George Washington's army, served dinner. Their boy, who had seen a blueberry pie cooling on the windowsill, cleaned his plate of meat and vegetables and drained two glasses of milk in record time.

"Please, Mother," he coaxed, "can I have a double helping of pie instead of just one?"

The answer came from the head of the table. "Tonight
you get no pie at all, young man. Maybe this will teach
you to come when you are called in future."

"Yes, sir, I'm sorry." There was disappointment but no
rebellion in the steel-gray eyes. The boy accepted his pun-
ishment in manly style, without lame excuses or whining
promises to do better if only he were pardoned this once.
He licked his lips longingly as his mother cut the juicy pie
into thick wedges, and he gulped when his father's fork
bit through the flaky crust into the blueberry filling.
"Please, sir," he said in torture, "may I be excused from
the table?"

"You may not! You will sit here and watch us enjoy our
dessert!" The Reverend Joseph Harvey believed in the
stern discipline of his Puritan ancestors. However, he
could temper justice with mercy and he relented now, in a
way the boy would appreciate. "Talking about your project
seems the same as food and drink to you, Charles," he continued. "Tell your mother and me about your latest ven-
ture. What are you building now?"

The blueberry pie all but forgotten, the boy plunged
eagerly into his favorite subject. "It's a bridge across the
brook, sir. I had to pick a kind of narrow place, and it
won't be able to hold up a regular wagon or team of horses
or anything like that, but it's going to be a real bridge. I
mean, it will hold me up, and a dog, and — you know." His
voice rose with excitement. "I ran errands down at the
sawmill and got them to pay me in laths. The framework
for the bridge is made out of laths. It's a brand-new construction idea that nobody ever thought of before. I figured it out myself."

The boy looked up to catch the fond smile his parents
exchanged as they thought him carried away by enthusiasm. "No, honest!" he protested proudly. "Mr. Nichols
came over to inspect the job this afternoon, and he says he

never saw a bridge built like mine anywhere along the whole Erie Canal. He's a sure-enough engineer, even if he is sort of old and retired, so he ought to know."

The Reverend Joseph Harvey and his wife hid another exchange of fond smiles. "I hope you didn't do any work on this brand-new construction idea yesterday while your mother and I were attending gospel-meeting in Hartford. Work done on the Sabbath is Satan's work, and no good can come of it."

"I didn't break the Sabbath, sir, and I never will," the boy promised his father seriously. "When I grow up and get to be a big builder of tunnels and bridges and canals and railroads, I'll have hundreds, maybe thousands, of men on my payrolls. But they won't be allowed to work on Sunday. No, sir, no matter what! Because one of the very first things built on any construction job of mine will be a church. I made up my mind about that a long time ago!"

At the age of twelve, Charles Harvey had made up his mind about his entire future. He intended to become a famous construction engineer. The next day, and for several days after going without blueberry pie for supper, he worked on his bridge. The summer sun slanted down on him through the trees as he placed lath after lath on a solid foundation. When the span reached across the brook, he started to cover it with a pathway made of clay.

Every morning and afternoon, other carefree boys would whistle past the busy builder, tempting him with reports of how the fish were biting at the pond or of how much spring there was in the new diving board at the swimming hole. He took their teasing with a good-natured grin, and stayed on the job. He quit work only once, and that was when the town bully came hulking around to do mischief.

The bully, three years older and half a head taller than the minister's son, was in his usual belligerent mood.

"You call that thing a bridge?" he jeered. "I could smash it with my bare feet! Watch me, and I'll show you how!"

"Try it!" The smaller boy, fists doubled, sprang in the other's path. His steel-gray eyes were steady and challenging. "Try it, and you'll be sorry!"

Although full of bluster and threatening gestures, the bully kept his distance. Something in the *gunfighter eyes* had stopped him in his tracks. Finally he shambled away, calling names and saying what he would do some other time.

That same afternoon Charles Harvey finished the bridge. It was ready for inspection and testing. He invited Mr. Nichols. The old Erie Canal engineer strolled up the road, the dented plug hat jaunty on his bald head and thumbs cocked in his polka-dot suspenders. He examined the bridge structure, nodding approval of the workmanship, and then called for the tests.

First the boy, full of confidence, walked across. Then he asked the man to do so. The bridge stood up under their weights with no sign of buckling. At last came the supreme test. Nervously the boy trundled a wheelbarrow full of stones to the center of the span. He held his breath in suspense.

Mr. Nichols raised his plug hat in a cheer. "Never budged," he chortled. "Couldn't have done a better job myself." His gnarled fingers reached out to give Charles Harvey a grave handshake. "You've got dreams in your eyes, son. Most boys get those dreams shaken loose by the time they grow up. Only a few men are able to make their boyhood dreams come true. I'm betting that you've got what it takes. There's room out West in the Great Lakes country for more bridges and railroads and such than a monkey could shake a stick at in a month of Sundays. Tell you what, son. First big construction job you get, send for yours truly, L. L. Nichols of the old Erie Canal, and I'll come out of retirement quicker than scat!"

"Thank you sir." The boy pumped the veteran engineer's right hand solemnly. "I sure will send for you, Mr. Nichols, because I'll need a good right-hand man, especially on my first big job!"

2

Eagle Feather

The scene with Mr. Nichols was one of the happiest of Charles Harvey's boyhood. Not long later, he had to rub the dreams from his eyes and face a very real and hard world. He gave up his ideas of going to college and becoming a trained engineer. When the Reverend Joseph Harvey fell upon hard times, his son felt it his duty to quit school and help support the family. At the age of fifteen, he found a job as clerk in a general store. It was a long way from bridge building, but his mother needed the money he brought home each Saturday.

A tavern was located across the road from where the boy hustled groceries and dry goods for customers. As the weeks and months went by, he began to hate strong drink because of what it did to men. He watched them stagger from the tavern, zigzag along the road, pitch headlong into the gutter. He saw wives and children huddled outside the door, crying for their husbands, and fathers to come home.

Ordinary people shook their heads and deplored the sights. It was characteristic of Charles Harvey to go ahead and do something about it. He organized a Cold Water Army, more than a hundred boys strong. They soon made life uncomfortable for the town's saloonkeepers. Not only did they invade bars and bring befuddled men outside to their waiting families, but they also reported any breaking of license laws to the police.

Brawny saloonkeepers tried to chase the boys away, but they were too nimble. They ducked around tables, scooted out the door, slipped in the back entrance to rescue men who had drunk themselves senseless. When the saloonkeepers found out that threats of violence had no effect on Charles Harvey, they went to his employers and threatened them with a large loss of trade unless the boy was fired.

The owners of the store supported their young employee, and, as a last resort, the saloonkeepers used trumped-up charges and perjured evidence to try to put the boy behind bars. They claimed he was maliciously ruining their business. The judge heard both sides of the story, rapped his gavel, and threw the case out of court. "Young man," he said, "keep up the good work!"

By this time seventeen-year-old Charles Harvey and his Cold Water Army were news. One morning he was told that the editor of the New England Weekly Review wanted to interview him. He could take the day off and catch a ride into nearby Hartford.

In the city he slipped off the tailgate of the wagon, brushed the hay from his clothes, and walked into the Review's office. He expected anything but the spectacle of a merry-eyed editor in sober Quaker garb, eating a slab of pie.

"Sit thee down, boy," he invited. "Our talk about your Cold Water Army can wait, but pie must be attended to at once." He served a generous portion across the desk and smiled his approval at the way Charles Harvey went to it. "My aunt has the reputation of making the best squash pies that were ever baked," he volunteered with some pride. "The whole Whittier family agrees on that."

"Whittier!" The boy choked on a mouthful of pie and his steel-gray eyes seemed to become twice as large. "You aren't John Greenleaf Whittier, the poet we studied in school?"

"Does it surprise thee to see a poet eating pie?" Mr.
Whittier chuckled. "Between thee and me, I think Ralph
Waldo Emerson and Henry Wadsworth Longfellow act too
much like harvest hands when it comes to pie. It is my belief that a proper restraint toward New England pie helps
shape character." He winked gravely. "For example, I
never allow myself more than two helpings at breakfast."

The boy laughed with the poet and joked of how his own
character had been shaped by blueberry-pie discipline.
After they had finished both the squash pie and the Cold
Water Army interview, Mr. Whittier brought out an eagle
feather. It had just been given to him by William Cullen
Bryant as a souvenir of the other poet's trip to the Lake
Superior region.

"Imagine this eagle plume were a magic carpet to carry
thee and me up there," the Quaker editor day-dreamed.
"We would sail through the clouds to a land of church-
steeple pines and sweet-water seas. Below us would appear
prospectors' tents and hillside scars where copper or iron
mines have been blasted. We would see the falls and rapids
of the St. Mary's River bottleneck that keeps ships from
passing into the greatest of the Great Lakes. Along the river
banks we would spy out wigwams and trading posts and the
house where explorer and historian Henry Rowe Schoolcraft wrote down the legends of the American Indians in
hopes that a poet might turn them into a national epic."

"Why don't you do it, sir?" the boy hero-worshipped.
"You could, easy!"

Mr. Whittier shook his head. "I thank thee for the compliment, friend, but my muse is for the shorter flights.
Here are a few verses I dashed off this morning as the eagle
plume brought pictures to my mind."

Charles Harvey felt a strange excitement hum through
his blood as he took the scratch-paper handed to him and
read the scribbled lines:

I hear the far-off voyager's horn,
I see the Yankee's trail —
His foot on every mountain pass,
On every stream his sail.

He's whistling round St. Mary's falls,
Upon his loaded train;
He's leaving on the Pictured Rocks
His fresh tobacco stain.

Behind the scared squaw's birch canoe,
The steamer smokes and raves;
And city lots are staked for sale
Above old Indian graves —

"There are more verses," admitted Mr. Whittier, "but mainly in the same slap-dash style. To do justice to School-craft's Ojibway legends of the Lake Superior country would be a long task. Perhaps I should say a *Long*fellow's task."

Chuckling over his pun, the Quaker picked up the eagle feather. "I have noticed thee admiring this plume. Accept it as a keepsake, friend, and may it bring thee good fortune. If thy travels ever take thee around Boston and Cambridge, call upon Professor Longfellow at Harvard, tell him about my pun on his name, and pass along the keepsake to him for inspiration. Who knows? Many a truth has been spoken in jest, and great projects have depended on lesser trifles than an eagle's plume!"

3

End of Navigation

From the moment he left the Weekly Review's Office, throughout the years leading to his young manhood, Charles Harvey cherished the eagle feather as a good-luck charm. Going from one job to another in New England, he climbed the ladder of success until, at the age of twenty-two, he became the star traveling salesman for the Fairbanks Scales Company of St. Johnsbury, Vermont.

One of the things that had made this young man the top sales agent of the firm was his driving ambition to buy his mother a piano. Each pair of scales he sold put him nearer his goal. He traveled far and fast, he worked early and late, he went without proper food and sleep. The vision of his mother's face when she would see the new piano, kept him going long beyond normal endurance, but finally even Charles Harvey's resistance fell so low that the germs began to win the battle.

He was in New York when the sickness struck, and he barely found strength to catch a train for Connecticut. He never afterwards remembered the ride, nor his walk from the railroad station, through the snow and slush to his home. Dizzy as a top and burning up with fever, he stumbled into the house and collapsed.

A doctor took one look and said, "Typhoid!" He offered the Reverend Joseph Harvey and his wife little hope for their son's recovery. For many days young Charles hovered between life and death. Then came the crisis, the critical hour which would decide his fate.

Mrs. Harvey came out of the sick room wringing her hands in despair. She threw herself into her husband's arms. "I'm afraid he's taken a turn for the worse," she sobbed. "He's delirious, and he thinks the eagle feather is a carpet. He talks about looking down from the clouds at tents and wigwams and seeing the house of somebody named Schoolcraft, and he just asked for a glass of cold Lake Superior water. The doctor gave in to him and let him drink all he wanted."

Thirty minutes after Charles Harvey called for Lake Superior water the crisis was past. The water he had been given came from the backyard pump, but in his delirium he saw it spill over St. Mary's Falls into the tumbler that he raised eagerly to his lips with the doctor's help. At any rate, the water broke the fever, brought on a healthful sweat, and started the patient on the road to recovery. To Reverend and Mrs. Harvey this was an answer to their fervent prayers.

In the spring with the maple trees turning green on the Vermont hills, the young traveling salesman reported back to work at the Scales Company. The three Fairbanks brothers — Joseph, Erastus and Thaddeus — treated him as if they were kindly uncles instead of his bosses.

"You've been through a hard siege," said Joseph, the lawyer of the firm. "We aren't going to let you go out on the road right away. You need a rest-cure. There's nothing more relaxing than a steamboat ride. You could combine business with pleasure by riding down the Mississippi to New Orleans, and selling Fairbanks Scales at every landing along the river."

"That's a good idea, but I've got a better one," chimed in Erastus, the business head of the firm. "There's nothing like an ocean voyage and salt air. We'll book passage for you on an Atlantic packet to Cuba. It's a good market for Fairbanks Scales and a fine lazy country to rest in."

"Why don't you let the boy speak for himself?" said
Thaddeus, the brother who had invented the famous scales
that were better known around the globe than any other
American product. "Anyone with half an eye can see that
he's got a place in mind. Go ahead, Charles. Tell us where
you'd like to go."

Ever since he had built the bridge and talked to Mr.
Nichols, ever since his meeting with John Greenleaf
Whittier, Charles Harvey had had an idea in the back of his
mind. Even in his sick delirium it had been there, an un-
explainable urge to take a trip to the Great Lakes, and to
see the greatest of all lakes.

"I wish you'd send me into the copper regions of Lake
Superior," he told the three bearded brothers, and then
tried a pun in Mr. Whittier's style. "I trust it would prove
a *superior* region to exchange scales for copper."

The Fairbanks brothers agreed to send their star salesman into the Lake Superior region for his rest-cure, but
they insisted that he stop off in Boston and get a physical
checkup from their good friend, Dr. Oliver Wendell Holmes,
who was becoming famous not only as a physician but as an
author as well.

"Healthy as young Hercules," reported Dr. Holmes after
examining Charles Harvey in his Boston office. "I'd choose
to be on your side in a fight, young man."

An hour later, having followed the road directions given
him by the self-styled Autocrat of the Breakfast Table, the
Connecticut Yankee strolled across the Harvard campus,
knocked at a Cambridge door, and handed his calling card
to the man who answered and said, "Yes, I'm Professor
Longfellow."

He had twinkling blue eyes in a Santa Claus face, and he
stroked his beard as he read aloud the main points of the

calling card. "Charles Thompson Harvey — Commercial Traveler — Chief Western Agent — Fairbanks Scales Company." He beckoned and then led the way into a study. "I'm not in the market for scales, my boy," he chuckled, pointing to a table piled with books, but I'll wager it would take a pair of your best platform models to weigh that mass of material."

At first, Charles Harvey glanced idly at the huge books, but when he saw the name of the author his attention was riveted. Everyone of the large volumes had been written by Henry Rowe Schoolcraft! Pulling a somewhat bedraggled eagle feather from his pocket, he gave it to Professor Longfellow as Mr. Whittier had asked him to do, and then he told the Cambridge poet about his meeting with the Quaker poet. "He said this eagle feather might inspire you to write an epic about the American Indians, sir. He made a pun on your name."

Professor Longfellow listened to the pun with relish. "A long task for a *Long*fellow, eh?" he smiled, and then became serious. "The hand of fate may be in this," he said. "By a strange coincidence I am about to study Mr. Schoolcraft's books about the Indians, and now you bring me an eagle plume for inspiration, and tell me that you are on your way to the very place where the legends were collected. Please give my respects to Mr. Schoolcraft's home when you reach the St. Mary's."

"I'll be sure to do that, sir," promised Charles Harvey, taking his leave to catch the train for Buffalo. It was a three-day trip by steamboat from that port to the End of Navigation on the Great Lakes, past Detroit, up the St. Clair River, across Lake Huron, and up the broad St. Mary's to where the falls and rapids plunged from Lake Superior to prevent ship passage any further.

The steamboat swung around to dock not far from a stately two-story home on the river bank. It stood out from the wigwams and shanties of the frontier outpost so that Charles Harvey recognized it at a glance. He whipped off his hat and bowed with a flourish: "Professor Longfellow," he said, "sends his respects!"

4

Nosiree, Bub!

The Schoolcraft house was vacant, and the Indian Department in Detroit had put a TO LET sign on the lawn. Promising himself that the day might come when he would be able to live in such a home, young Charles Harvey rented a room at the boarding house run by Mrs. Bingham, wife of the Baptist minister. Everyone liked the young boarder and tried to put the roses back in his cheeks. Kate, the minister's pretty daughter, made eyes at him and saw to it that he was given the most comfortable rocking chair on the porch.

From this rocking chair during the next day or so, young Harvey saw an opportunity to make history, and he set out to make it!

Here are the things he could see from the front porch: a pioneer town of fish shanties and fur trading posts on the rambling shores of St. Mary's Falls; Ojibway braves bobbing in their canoes as they speared whitefish in the whirlpools below the rapids; the whitewashed walls of Fort Brady on the American side of the river, and the Canadian landmark of a Hudson Bay Post on the opposite shore.

Wanting to be active, young Harvey squirmed in the rocking chair as Mrs. Bingham and Kate scolded him about continuing his rest-cure. He stared at the surging bottleneck of black rocks and white water that not only separated Canada from the United States but also kept mighty Lake Superior from her sister lakes — Huron, Michigan, Erie,

Ontario — and the whole Inland Waterway that finally ran out the St. Lawrence River into the Atlantic Ocean and the Seven Seas.

From the porch, young Harvey could see the ribs of a cargo ship that had tried to run the rapids years ago, and now lay shattered on the rocks. He saw how all up-bound boats, unable to face the fury of the rapids, had to dock below town. He saw their cargoes shifted to a portage railroad, which consisted of clumsy freight cars pulled by mule teams along the iron rails that snaked up the main street. Then he saw the ship cargoes reloaded aboard other boats waiting above the rapids.

Was this, Charles Harvey wondered, the only way supplies and machinery could be transported to the mining towns on Lake Superior? No. Now and then, he found, entire ships were taken out of the water below the rapids, hoisted on rollers and greased skids, and hauled up the main street to where they could be lowered back into the water above the falls.

When Charles Harvey saw a three-masted sailing ship pulled foot by foot through town, he decided it was time to stop being sick. It was Sault Ste. Marie that needed doctoring!

With the curiosity and enthusiasm of a boy who was a born salesman, young Harvey escaped from the watchful eyes of Kate and Mrs. Bingham. He went around town asking countless questions. Why hadn't someone thought of building a canal around the rapids?

Oldtimers were amused by the youth's excitement. Someone *had* thought of a canal, Bub, several years ago, but the contractors had gotten cold feet at the size of the job and wiggled out of their contract with the State of Michigan. Besides, the portage railroads were opposed to a canal, because it would run them out of business.

Furthermore, the oldtimers said, a canal would take jobs away from the men who were hauling ships on rollers. It would put stevedores out of business. Why, Bub, the whole town of Sault Ste. Marie would be nothing but a ghost town. The ships would sail right through the canal and pass us by. Our hotels and boarding houses and eating places would go bankrupt.

Nosiree, Bub, we like things the way they are. You try to go ahead with any foolish ideas about a canal and we'll fight — the same way Erie, Pennsylvania is fighting.

You've heard about the Erie War, haven't you, Bub? And how those railroad companies are trying to put in the same size tracks so trains won't have to stop at Erie and let folks change cars to another line? We don't want any smart aleck to put us in Erie's shoes!

Young Harvey never wasted time arguing, but he was thinking: You can't stop progress, you can't let a *few* people stop something that's good for a *lot* of people.

He knew the oldtimers weren't taking him seriously. The Soo was anything but a temperance town, and they made fun of his favorite drink, raspberry shrub. They said that, in the first place, nobody could build a canal at the Soo, and in the second place, even if somebody could, it wouldn't be a *tee*total sissy!

They reminded him of Henry Clay's famous remark: You know what *he* said about it, don't you, Bub? He said, why don't you try building a canal on the moon? It makes the same kind of sense and isn't much further away!

The oldtimers laughed up their sleeves at young Harvey as he continued to roam the Soo, questioning trappers, traders, voyageurs, Ojibways, prospectors, immigrants in broadcloth or homespun or hand-me-downs, saltwater sailors, and freshwater skippers who thought the oceans were puddles compared with the Great Lakes.

"Got day-dreams about building a canal up here at the end of nowhere, huh, Bub?" the oldtimers jeered. "Going to dig a ditch from Lake Superior around the rapids and hook it up to the other lakes? Going to turn a paddle-and-portage river into an international seaway of commerce? Well, you can dream, but you can't do it, Bub! This is wilderness country, too far from civilization and always will be. It's four hundred miles to the nearest machine shop at Saginaw, and Dee-troit's even further. The Soo isn't even part of the United States six months a year. It's locked up in ice and snow, and winter throws away the key!"

Young Charles Harvey looked and listened, and never lost his temper. One day he went down to the steamboat landing as the sidewheeler *Illinois* was docking. Captain Jack Wilson gave a friendly wave and tossed his young friend a copy of the *Detroit Free Press*.

"Big news breaking," he called through his speaking trumpet. "The Congress in Washington is having a hot argument about whether to allow Michigan to build a canal by means of paying a private contractor with public lands for doing the job."

"Do you think the lands are valuable enough to make it worth while for a company like mine to bid for the contract?" Harvey asked.

Captain Jack Wilson squinted at the rapids roaring down from Lake Superior. "Plenty iron and copper and pine up yonder," he replied. "Go take a look at it. Seeing's believing, son!"

Young Harvey took the next steamer from the head of the rapids. The boat went past the Pictured Rocks to Iron Bay and Copper Harbor. He toured the iron mines in the hills above Marquette, eating pasties with the Cornishmen and taking their advice on which would be the most likely lands to claim. He drew maps and made lists of mineral fields and thick stands of timber.

He also — true to his calling as a salesman — showed drawings and models of Fairbanks Scales to the iron company officials. But his heart was not in his work. Deep in his heart he already had resigned as a salesman for the Fairbanks Scales Company of St. Johnsbury, Vermont. He was a traveling salesman for the Soo Canal — and he traveled!

On Keweenaw Peninsula he saw prehistoric copper pits that had been mined long before Columbus sighted America. The last doubt left his mind when he saw a chunk of virgin copper as big as a house.

"How much does it weigh?" a veteran prospector echoed his question. "Upwards of five hundred tons, son. Pretty hefty nugget, even for this part of the country!"

With two lists of valuable mineral and timber lands in his pocket, young Harvey hurried back to Sault Ste. Marie. It was August 26, 1852. Captain Jack Wilson steamed into town a few days later with a Detroit paper that said:

PRESIDENT FILLMORE SIGNS CANAL BILL
Congress Grants Michigan Right Of Way And Donation Of Public Land For Construction Of Ship Canal Around Falls Of St. Mary's.

Harvey enclosed the newspaper clipping in a letter to his employers. "This is the opportunity of a lifetime," he wrote them. "My lists of land will pay for the cost of a canal many times over. The Soo Canal will open up the treasures of Lake Superior, now locked to the world. Please give me permission to investigate the possibilities."

5

Preliminary Skirmishes

The time seemed endless until an answer arrived from Vermont. Young Harvey opened the letter with trembling fingers, then he tossed his hat in the air and smiled all over. The three Fairbanks brothers made no rash promises to finance the canal, but they gave their salesman permission to look into the matter for them.

A boyhood vision flashed across Charles Harvey's mind. Once again he was standing beside a backyard bridge and shaking hands with a gnarled engineer. "I sure will send for you, Mr. Nichols, because I'll need a good right-hand man, especially on my first big job!"

He sent for Mr. L. L. Nichols, and the old Erie Canal engineer came out of his retirement in Connecticut. "Told you I'd come quicker than scat," he chuckled. "Let's spit on our hands and dig in, son!"

The first important job was to make a preliminary survey for the canal. As they drove their stakes and took sights, a crowd gathered. There were ominous threats. A burly spokesman for the portage railroad shook his fist and yelled:

"The crazy young fool must be anxious to start an Indian war. He's surveying a canal that will cut through an ancient Ojibway burial ground."

Young Harvey's steel-gray eyes began to blaze like those of a frontier gunfighter. He picked up a stake and waited for violence. But nothing happened — then. His show of fight had made the bullies think twice. The next moment,

Kate Bingham, the minister's daughter, stepped to his side and put her small hand in his.

The crowd, grumbling, moved away. Mr. Nichols whipped out a red handkerchief and wiped his brow. "Whew!' he said. "That was close, son!"

By November, the canal survey was completed and shipped to Vermont. As winter closed in on the Soo, young Harvey decided to take his plans down to Lansing and submit them to the Michigan Legislature. He built castles in the air. In fact, as the steamboat pulled away from the landing, he had his eyes glued on the TO LET sign in front of Schoolcraft's former residence. He dreamed of making it Canal Headquarters, where he could entertain distinguished guests, perhaps a king or a president.

As soon as the steamboat docked in Detroit, he called on the Office of Indian Affairs. The man in charge listened to his request with growing bewilderment. "You want to lease Elmwood for the Soo Canal Company, an outfit that doesn't exist yet — except in your imagination. And you say all you got to do is get a canal bill passed in Lansing and then sell your own employers on the idea of putting up the money to build this canal that's just a gleam in your eye?"

"Yes, sir," said Charles Harvey stoutly, ignoring the official's sarcasm. "The gleam in my eye is going to become a sparkling mile of water that will give ships a passage into Lake Superior."

"You say so, huh?" The official grunted doubtfully. "Well, I'll make out the lease on Elmwood when you've got the canal contract in your pocket — and not a minute before!"

"I'll be back in the spring," young Harvey said, and he took the train of cars for Lansing. Most of the lawmakers in Michigan's state capital gave him a cold shoulder, but he found a strong champion in Judge William Austin Burt.

"I'm proud to meet you, Judge Burt," Harvey said in a hero-worshipping voice. "It's a great honor to shake hands with the man who discovered all the Lake Superior iron ranges, from Michigan's Marquette to Minnesota's Mesabi."

The grizzled old Iron Hunter beamed and led the way into his private office. He showed young Harvey his inventions, an equatorial sextant; a typographer, father of the modern typewriter; and an instrument that resembled a complicated sundial.

"My solar compass," he explained proudly. "Queen Victoria's husband, Prince Albert, gave me a prize for it last year at the World's Fair in London's Crystal Palace. I talked to him, face to face, same as I'm talking to you. 'Sure,' I told him, 'I discovered the Iron Ranges, but, if it hadn't been for this solar compass of mine, I wouldn't have known where I was or how to get back. Ordinary compasses aren't worth three cents out in the Iron Hills. They just spin around every which way and go crazy!'" Judge Burt chuckled. "Never mind an old man bragging, son. What can I do for you?"

"A canal into Lake Superior would open up all those Iron Ranges you discovered," Harvey said earnestly. "I need your help to get the Canal Bill passed, sir."

"I'm Chairman of the Committee and you can count on my support," Judge Burt promised, "but you've got stormy sailing ahead. They'll call you an unlicked cub and they'll say you're too young for any such job."

"I won't hear them," grinned Harvey. "I'll wear earmuffs!"

It was Judge Burt who introduced Harvey to James Jesse Strang, the strangest figure in Michigan's legislative history. "You get some queer fish in every barrel," the former Iron Hunter said, "and the same applies to Lansing's politicians, only more so. Take King Strang, for instance, the only king ever crowned in the United States, and it happened right on Big Beaver Island in Lake Michigan, only a stone's throw from the Straits of Mackinac, and right down the Snowshoe Pike from Sault Ste. Marie."

"King Strang?" Harvey echoed, his eyes bulging. "You mean the Mormon leader who is a" — he had trouble with the word — "polygamist?"

"They say he's got a wife for every day in the week. All I know is, he's got the reputation of being able to pick the prettiest girls and the workingest mules on the Lakes." Judge Burt winked. "A canal can get along fine without girls, son, but it's got to have mules!"

King Strang had a friendly handshake for young Harvey. He was a short stocky man with red hair and eyes that were flaming swords. "I'll not only back your Canal Bill," he said, "but, once you start to dig the big ditch, I'll keep you supplied with the best mules on the Great Lakes."

Thanks to men like Judge Burt and King Strang, the Canal Bill finally was presented to the main body of the Michigan Legislature. Harvey had to appear on the floor and defend his cause. He faced a barrage of catcalls from the the balcony and taunts from the lawmakers themselves:

"Look at the whippersnapper who wants us to give him a canal contract! He isn't even dry behind the ears yet! He's still got a hold on his mother's apron strings!"

"How much experience has he had? Ask him what he ever built! A toy bridge in his backyard when he was twelve years old!"

"Come back and talk to us after you grow up, Harvey! You're nothing but a boy! Canal-building is a man-sized job!"

Harvey tightened his fists. His gunfighter eyes swept the crowd. "I may be young, but I'm man-sized and I stand ready to prove it to anyone!"

There was no response to Harvey's challenge. Michigan's lawmakers, impressed by his spunk, passed the Canal Bill and offered his company first chance at the contract. Harvey, who had been keeping the wires hot all winter, sent a last eloquent telegram to St. Johnsbury, Vermont.

The three Fairbanks Brothers threw up their hands in defeat. "People will have to admit we picked a good salesman," Erastus, the business manager, said dryly. "He just sold us a canal!"

"And he's only twenty-three!" fretted Joseph, the lawyer.

"More power to him!" Thaddeus, the inventor, stroked his beard, and his voice was wistful. "I wish I was his age again!"

When Harvey received word that the Fairbank Brothers would form a company with other Eastern capitalists to build the Soo Canal, he danced a sailor's hornpipe around his Lansing hotel room with Judge Burt. But the old Iron Hunter put a damper on his enthusiasm.

"We passed the Canal Bill," he admitted, "but the anti-canal crowd set a bear trap in it. You've got a deadline to meet. Unless you finish the job within two years after starting work, you forfeit the land grant — 750,000 acres of choice timber and mineral property. By the way, son, do you have an extra copy of your land lists so I can borrow it and check to see if your ideas of valuable locations agree with mine?"

"Yes, sir," said Harvey. "I keep an extra copy in the drawer of this desk, and you're welcome to — " His voice trailed away as his fingers failed to find the sheets of paper. A closer search revealed that the desk had been ransacked. The papers were gone.

"Land speculators," Judge Burt decided instantly. "They stole your extra copies while you were waiting word from Vermont in my office. That means they have about a four-hour start to Dee-troit and the first steamboat bound for the Soo. They'll file claim at the Land Office up there on every piece of property you've got listed. They figure to make a tidy profit on the choice lands and leave your company with second-rate timber and mineral holdings."

"They haven't beaten me to the Soo yet," said Harvey as he bolted out the door on his way to the train depot.

6

Full Steam Ahead

Harvey arrived on the Detroit waterfront only to find that a group of men, notorious as land speculators, had chartered the fast steamer *Northerner* and were well started toward the Soo. His frantic eyes spotted the familiar outline of the sidewheeler *Illinois,* and he sprinted for its dock.

Captain Jack Wilson sized up the situation. "We can show a clean pair of heels to the *Northerner* in a fair race, but there's nothing fair about a three-hour head start." He squinted at Harvey's dismal countenance. "Get down to the engine room and tell the firemen to throw on a tub of lard with every load of cordwood. The *Illinois* may not arrive first, but she'll bust her boilers trying!"

Harvey, bare to the waist, helped stoke the fire as the sidewheeler bowled up the Detroit River past Windmill Point, across Lake St. Clair, and up the swift St. Clair River where the drift ice of late spring snapped at the steamer's bows. When he came up on deck for his first breath of fresh air, night had fallen and the *Illinois* was pitching across stormy Saginaw Bay in Lake Huron. The sparks flew out of the tall smoke stacks like shooting stars.

Down below again, Harvey ordered two tubs of lard thrown on with every load of cord-wood. The flames whooshed as the lard exploded, and the *Illinois* leaped ahead as if it were being towed by a frightened sturgeon. After one look at the boiler pressure, the chief engineer's face seemed to turn green.

34

The sidewheeler was ramming down the ice-choked throat of the St. Mary's River the next day, when a roar from Captain Jack Wilson brought Harvey up on deck. Sault Ste. Marie lay less than a mile ahead and the *Illinois* had overhauled the *Northerner.* They were racing side by side through thickening ice floes, both losing momentum.

Harvey made a quick decision as the sidewheeler scraped and fought for a passage. Black with smoke from the engine room and still bare to the waist he slid down a line at the bow as Captain Wilson jammed the *Illinois* into the ice along the American shore. Harvey skidded on the slippery surface at breakneck speed and wished he had skates on his shoes. A wide blue crack in the ice almost gave the race to the land speculators who were still plowing ahead aboard the *Northerner,* but he took a running broadjump and reached the opposite edge with nothing to spare but his flying heels. Safe on the riverbank, he sprinted across Elmwood's front yard to take the Fort Brady short-cut to Water Street. Behind him came the baffled shouts of anger from the land speculators; ahead of him loomed startled faces under coal-skuttle bonnets, Ojibway feather-bands, racoon caps, voyageur kerchiefs, and beaver hats.

A round-eyed clerk watched Harvey skid to a stop and push two lists of lands across the counter of the U. S. Land Office. He was not used to having a shirtless and beardless apparition tell him to: "File these and hold them in reserve. The Soo Canal Company is claiming first choice on 750,000 acres of mineral and timber property in Michigan."

Unaware that he was filing lands that would yield untold treasures in iron and copper and white pine, the clerk handled the lists in routine fashion. "Soo Canal Company?" he echoed. "Never heard tell of it."

"You will!" Harvey promised with a broad smile. "From now on!"

On his way back to the *Illinois*, he yanked the TO LET sign from Elmwood's lawn. Down in Detroit again, he presented the sign to the official at the Department of Indian Affairs. "You can put this away for a while," he said, "and make out a two-year lease on the place. We won't need it any longer because that's the deadline on the canal contract."

Flabbergasted by Harvey's success and by his delivery of the sign, the official was still sarcastic and doubtful. "Better take out an option to renew the lease," he advised. "You might not make your deadline!"

Harvey brushed any such thought from his mind as he boarded a train to take the canal contract back East to his employers. On the way he had to change cars at Erie, Pennsylvania, and in walking from one station to another, he saw what newspaper headlines were calling *The Erie War*.

The skies were red above Erie. Ashes from blazing buildings fell on Harvey's clothes. Acrid smoke made him cough. He elbowed a path through yelling mobs wild with excitement. The citizens were up in arms against railroad workers who were trying to change all tracks to standard size so passengers would not have to get out and change cars at every whistlestop along the line.

Afraid that it would mean loss of business for them if there was no stopover, the townspeople of Erie were piling up railroad tracks and making bonfires of railroad equipment. The governor had called out the state militia, but the mobs dared the soldiers to stop them.

Harvey, fighting his way to the next train, gulped in dismay at the sight of men and women gone berserk. He was troubled by this vision of what might happen if the citizens of Sault Ste. Marie went on the warpath against the canal.

Other worries took charge of his mind once he arrived at William and Wall Street in New York City and was ushered into the conference room where the financial backers of the Canal Company started to elect officers as soon as he handed them the contract from Michigan.

It seemed no place for a young man, this Board of Directors meeting, rich with the aroma of expensive cigars and the wink of valuable rings. Harvey fidgeted between President Corning of the New York Central Railroad and Erastus Fairbanks, newly elected Governor of Vermont as well as business manager of the scales factory. Across the table sat August Belmont, the international banker, already Ambassador to Spain.

When all the directors were elected, the Fairbanks Brothers recommended their star salesman as General Agent of the Canal Company. But there were strong objections. Harvey flushed and squirmed in his chair as his youth and inexperience were pointed out and held against him. He wanted to sink through the floor. These men had long beards, and long bank accounts to match. His dollars were as few and far apart as his whiskers. He stared anxiously at the cautious, distrustful faces. He was going to be fired even before he was hired!

"Please gentlemen!" He sprang to his feet in desperate appeal. "Just give me a chance! Remember, there's strength in youth, and a young man has the courage of his inexperience and ignorance. Sometimes he goes ahead and does things that never were done before, simply because he doesn't have the sense or training to recognize what's impossible!"

Thaddeus Fairbanks, the inventor, chuckled and several other directors hid sympathetic smiles with their hands, but a whitehaired banker spoke up for most of the room. "The point is," he said in a cold and calculating voice, "that young men are reckless and irresponsible. The job under discussion will require decisions involving large sums of money and credit. This young man is not financially responsible for such a position of trust. Who will be his surety?"

After a hurried consultation with his brothers, Erastus Fairbanks addressed the meeting. "The young man tips our scales at one hundred thousand dollars. We'll back him for that sum — and more, if necessary!"

The quiet words ended all argument and they made Charles Harvey feel ten feet tall. He could have crowed like a rooster. He was Mr. Charles T. Harvey, General Agent, St. Mary's Falls Ship Canal Company, Sault Ste. Marie, Upper Peninsula, Michigan!

The directors tried to temper his exuberance by telling him that they would send a chief engineer and a super-intendent of construction as soon as they could find men of fitting calibre, but young Harvey never gave it a second thought.

As General Agent, he intended to boss the works!

Thaddeus Fairbanks broke into his day-dreams. "Congratulations, son," he said. "This means a salary increase, of course. Got any plans for spending the extra money?"

"You bet I have sir," Charles Harvey replied. "Now I can finally buy my mother the piano she's been wanting so long."

7

War Drums

Two weeks after hearing his mother play the new piano, and twelve days before his twenty-fourth birthday, the former traveling salesman showed his men how to use a shovel, and he hauled the first wheelbarrow of dirt from the canal cut.

He had arrived at the Soo on the steamer *Illinois* with four hundred men, several teams of King Strang mules, necessary tools and supplies.

Within forty-eight hours he had erected shanties to house the men; he had organized a commissary to supply regular meals; he had begun a hospital on Rapid's Island; he had opened a quarry on Drummond Island; he had located a logging camp at Garden River; and he had occupied Elmwood as the company residence and general headquarters.

Now he had started digging the world's greatest canal. And he had nothing in his favor but youth and determination. He had never so much as put up a picket fence or built a wooden sidewalk.

It was June 4, 1853, a day to go down in the history books.

But the hostile bystanders sneered. Just wait a while. The young upstart would lose his steam and then he'd be the goat. It would take more than a raw cub to build a canal at the jumping-off place of creation inside of two years.

Wait and see!

The trouble was, Harvey moved so fast he was hard to see!

The first reports he mailed back to the company directors took their breath away. They forgot about sending a chief engineer and a construction superintendent. Their General Agent was handling everything.

He even insisted on giving his men health and accident insurance. At first the canal gangs kicked about the twenty-five cents premium deducted from their wages each pay-day, but it only took one accident to change their minds. An Indiana shovelman had his leg broken by a flying rock exploded out of the canal cut by a charge of blasting powder, and he thanked Harvey for three months' vacation with full pay.

A nickname for the boss began to be whispered along the cut and in the shanties. *Young Mister Big!* The Irish started the expression and the canal gangs never stopped using it. "Young Mister Big," they said, "does everything but tuck us into our bunks at night!"

Even so, it was hard to keep men on the job. They deserted by the scores at word of a rich strike at Iron Bay or Copper Harbor in Lake Superior. The vaguest rumor lured them into the wilderness.

Harvey solved the situation by sending agents to meet every immigrant boat that docked at Boston or Philadelphia or New York. He even hired fabulous Old Cap Sparhawk with his paddlewheeler the *Prairie Dew* and his equally fabulous young sidekick Captain Thunder Bay McCargo who sailed the schooner *Minong*. They were the greatest skippers on the Great Lakes, and men followed them as naturally as rats followed the Pied Piper.

"Tell these immigrants we're digging a ditch into the lake that wears an iron collar and a copper crown," Harvey said to Sparhawk and McCargo. "Tell them this is a job they can brag about to their grandchildren!"

Bustled and bundled aboard the *Prairie Dew* and the *Minong* almost before their ships made landfall in America, hundreds of immigrants were delivered to the Soo by Sparhawk and McCargo. They were mostly Scots and Irish, Germans and Swedes. They generally took one dismayed look at the Soo and uttered a national exclamation: "Hoot, mon!" "Glory Be!" "Yumpin' Yimminy!" However, many families, now famous, got their first start toward fortune in the ditch that his opponents called Harvey's Folly.

The young engineer sensed an undercurrent of opposition to his work progress, but he found it hard to track down. A favorite trick was to wheel grog wagons into the cut when he was on the job somewhere else, and sell dippers of whisky to the canal gangs.

Harvey issued himself an axe from the tool shed. The next time he spotted a grog wagon in the cut, he grabbed the axe. Two minutes later the ground was drinking whisky and the wagon was a splintered wreck.

After that he had less trouble, until he heard Indian drums start to talk up and down the St. Mary's River.

He walked down to the rapids. Across on the Canadian shore, he could see young chiefs of his own age decked out in war paint. Soon a bugle sounded an alarm from nearby Fort Brady. The tiny garrison began to parade back and forth with bristling guns. It was a brave show but what could a token force of soldiers do against the aroused Ojibways?

An old trader, Peter Barbeau, told Harvey what must have happened. "The anti-canal crowd has given the young chiefs plenty of firewater. They've put a bug in redskin ears about how you're cutting through their ancient burial grounds with your ditch. It's a nasty business, son, and if these young chiefs ever get loose from old Chief Tall

Pine, there's no telling what might explode — maybe a massacre!"

Across at the Canadian Soo there was wild excitement. Harvey noticed that the young chiefs and their followers were arguing heatedly with old Chief Tall Pine. A few hotheaded braves already were piling into their canoes. Tall Pine made angry motions for them to stay until he gave orders.

On his own side of the river, Harvey told his nervous canal gangs to stay on the job and above all not to fire at an Indian. Then he took a birchbark canoe from the beach and pushed it into the stream. His paddle dipped toward the opposite shore. As the canoe scraped sand again, his heart was beating twice as fast as the war drums.

The young chiefs muttered at his approach. One of them lifted a plumed lance threateningly. He walked a gauntlet of flashing eyes and stepped straight to Chief Tall Pine.

"I am a young chief," he told the aged Ojibway leader, partly in English, partly in sign language, "and a young chief does not always listen to an old chief. Sometimes this is good. But how can it be good when the young chiefs are full of firewater? Then the old chief should not waste his time talking. He should keep them home and out of mischief.

"Your young chiefs say they will stop my canal because it goes through your ancient burial grounds. This is the firewater speaking, the bad medicine they were given by my enemies.

"Your young chiefs want to fight about dead men's bones. This can only end in more dead men's bones, white men and red men.

"Keep your young chiefs at home, Chief Tall Pine. When the firewater is burned from their hearts, tell them that new life for a continent will flow through the ancient bur-

ial ground so that the Ojibways may be proud of their part
in the Soo Canal. I have spoken!"

Young Harvey, his spine tingling but his face showing
no fear, turned his back on Chief Tall Pine and the war-
painted braves; then he pushed the birchbark canoe out
into the stream. The roar of the falls filled his ears. Or
was it the roar of the Indians hitting the war path? He
dipped his paddle deep and dared not look around until he
reached the opposite shore because the Ojibways might in-
terpret it as a sign of fear — and they always attacked
any show of weakness.

Suddenly, the drums stopped beating. Harvey's heart
skipped a beat as he looked around. Then, as the drums
continued their silence and the Indians faded into the forest, his pulses slowed to normal.

Peter Barbeau, the old trader, helped haul the canoe up
on the bank. "It's lucky you got barbed wire for nerves,
son," he said. "Otherwise the Soo might be just a burnt
spot on the map, with every last one of our scalps dangling
from an Ojibway belt! Even if you don't succeed in building your canal, you can pride yourself on saving the Soo!"

8

Last Boat Out

As he had clashed with Michigan's bearded lawmakers, young Harvey soon clashed with Colonel Canfield, the government engineer, a clash that was again typical of the different viewpoints of youth and age.

The Colonel's methods were slow and irritating to Harvey; Harvey's slapdash speed was a thorn in the Colonel's side.

Strangely enough, it was Harvey's makeshift system of excavation that proved twice as effective at only half the cost of the Colonel's system.

And it was Harvey who refused to cut corners in spite of the Colonel's advice to save on this or that.

"I'm not putting anything but the best into this canal," Harvey said firmly. "It's going to be number one, not second rate!"

The Colonel called him a brainless puppy and he was Harvey's enemy from then on. He doddered around, devoting all his efforts to a pair of pet projects that he claimed for himself alone: the important coffer dam and the vital government charts.

Harvey trusted the Colonel and plunged ahead with his own work. As the summer advanced into the autumn of 1853, the self-trained young engineer sent Sparhawk and McCargo out to scour the Lakes for more workmen. He said he wanted sixteen hundred shovels in the big ditch by fall.

He built thirty more work shanties, with a married couple in each to supervise and do the cooking for fifty men.

The young boss with the firm jaw and the wide-set, far-sighted, gunfighter eyes became a familiar figure along the cut.

The mouse-colored pony he rode would flatten its ears and run for safety along with the canal gangs as the powder monkeys in the big ditch let loose another blast.

Every night Harvey sat at the table where Schoolcraft once had collected the legends of the Ojibways, the legends which Henry Wadsworth Longfellow now was studying back in Cambridge, Massachusetts. Here, in the Elmwood residence, a former traveling salesman from Vermont scribbled figures and counted time on his fingers.

From the foot to the head of the St. Mary's rapids, he had to dig a ditch that measured a mile and a little bit more, a ditch as deep as two tall men, as wide as a boulevard in Paris.

Once it was dug, he would have to line it with limestone; the rough limestone blocks from his own quarry on Drummond Island, and finished marble from the quarries at Maulden, Ontario, and Sandusky, Ohio.

He hired a fleet of twenty-five schooners to start hauling the huge blocks necessary for the sloping sides and deep floor of his ditch.

He sent to Beaver Island in Lake Michigan for more mule teams, and King Strang took time out from ruling his tiny Mormon Empire to keep his promise of supplying the canal with the workingest mules on the Lakes.

As the ditch grew deeper, young Harvey figured out a tackle and hoist system to lower the mules to their jobs and lift them out again when the whistle blew.

Housewives at the Soo shaded their eyes and stared at the huge piles of dirt and rock. Peeking over their wash lines or out their windows, they shook their heads and marveled: "That crazy young fool Harvey!"

But Kate Bingham, the minister's pretty daughter, smiled and waved as the mouse-colored pony with its erect rider passed the verandah of the Baptist mission. Kate knew what the canal gangs had nicknamed him, and he was the same in her eyes: *Young Mister Big!*

With the last boat out for the season in early October, Harvey knew that he was isolated from civilization for at least six months to come.

His only contact with the outside world would be the Snowshoe Pike: south from the Soo, across the frozen Straits of Mackinac, through the pine barrens of the Lower Peninsula, and down to the stage line at Saginaw that connected with the railroad at Detroit.

Only a few hardy adventurers ever took the Snowshoe Pike. The solitary regular traveler was the Ojibway mailman. He made the round trip once a month, shuffling along on his webbed bear-paw racquets.

Harvey realized that now, if ever, his enemies would strike. He finally had them spotted. They were the editor of the weekly newspaper, the *Soo Sentinel,* the heads of the portage railroad companies, and the principal land speculators who had lost out in the race for the Land Office — which also was the office of the newspaper.

These ringleaders met in the Wolverine Tavern every night. They drank hot buttered rum and plotted against the canal.

Harvey's first warning of real trouble came with the first snowfall of the season.

A boss lumberjack burst into Canal Headquarters at Elmwood early one morning. "We can't use the logging road to our main camp," he reported. "They've bought the rights to a thin strip of land between here and camp, and we can't get across because they've posted no-trespass signs."

Harvey scowled. "They've got no right to block us off from our own property. The law wouldn't allow it."

The middleaged lumberjack looked pityingly at the young general Agent. "There's no law at the Soo in wintertime," he reminded him. "What are we supposed to do? Wait for the Circuit Judge to come riding up here next summer? The bonfires along the cut are running out of wood. The canal gangs will freeze!"

Harvey thought a moment. It was a hard decision — to take the law into his own hands — but men's lives were at stake and he was responsible.

"Don't pay any attention to the signs," he ordered abruptly. "Use the logging road and get that wood to the canal cut!"

He stared out the frosty window, watching the dying bonfires, and his jaw went out an extra inch. Let the tavern ringleaders do their worst!

They had the brass and the gall to come calling on him that afternoon, reminding him that they owned the land and his men had no right to trespass. They were sanctimonious. Butter wouldn't melt in their mouths!

Harvey told them they had bought the land only to hurt the canal, and they had no right to freeze his men out.

When they threatened him, he doubled his fists and came charging out from behind the battered desk.

Their coat-tails whisked out the door, and they didn't talk loud again until they were safe in their sleigh.

They hatched another plan in the Wolverine Tavern that evening, and hired a rapscallion timber crew of half-breeds who came sneaking across the St. Mary's River during the night and chopped down trees to block the logging road.

It took a good part of the day for Harvey's lumberjacks to re-open the road, and once again the bonfires started to die.

Harvey was determined not to be caught napping again. Anticipating another attempt to block the logging road that night, he turned his woods camp into an armed camp and organized his lumberjacks into an army.

There was a full moon sparkling on the snow, and they waited behind a bend in the road for the rascally timber crew to show up.

At the first sound of an axe biting into wood, Harvey swung his men into formation and marched them down the road, husky loggers decked out in caulked boots, stagged pants, checkered mackinaws, red sashes and bright tasseled stocking caps.

They marched with axe handles on their shoulders, and Harvey was beating a big tin wash tub that sounded like a whole brass band.

The halfbreed timber crew listened in wonder, and when Harvey's army double-timed into sight around the bed of the logging road, they threw down their axes and saws in panic, and didn't stop running until they were on the safe side of the river.

That was the end of the lumber-jack war, and the bon-fires blazed high.

9

White Jungle

But Harvey's greatest enemy that winter was the great white cold that swirled down from Hudson Bay in winds that cut like torture whips and blizzards that smothered the world.

The camp cooks never had to worry about refrigeration. They hung huge beef carcasses outside the shanties and hacked off frozen slabs with their axes for mealtimes.

Zero weather was considered a warm spell. Sometimes the temperature dropped to thirty-five below, and now and then the mercury in the thermometers burst and nobody knew how cold it was.

To safeguard his canal crews, young Harvey kept the bonfires blazing to the skies. He stationed watchers at the end of each wheelbarrow line. When a watcher detected the tell-tale signs of white frost on a worker's nose or cheeks, he pushed him toward the fire, scrubbed snow on his face, and made him take a rest.

There were other men hired by Harvey to do nothing but slap circulation back into the limbs of workers.

The Canal Hospital on Rapid's Island took wonderful care of frostbite victims, but, in spite of all Harvey's precautions, men wandered away into the white jungle of snow and were never seen again.

The Irish said they were crazed by the great white cold. There was talk of *banshees, loup garous*, and Michigan's own *carcajou*, the mythical monster that feeds on men who dare the dangers of winter in the Lake Superior wilderness.

Harvey scoffed at these tall tales. A practical Yankee, he knew what the men needed — a chance to toast their hands and feet at the bonfires, plenty of scalding-hot tea, and a giant supper to give them energy for the next day.

He did his best, but his best was not enough to save everyone from the violence of winter, and the skullduggery of the canal's enemies.

The climax was reached when his right-hand man, John Tallman Whiting, brought him a typical report: "After last night's blizzard, we can't find one of our tool sheds, and a team of mules has disappeared. They must be buried in a snowdrift. Two more men wandered off, crazy-like, and we probably won't find their bodies until spring. A worker from Shanty Forty-nine was found frozen into an ice statue at dawn this morning, only a few yards from that grog shop at the corner of Water Street and Portage Trail."

Harvey smashed the desk with his fist. "That settles it," he snapped. "We've got some calls to make!"

The two big men, one of them hardly more than a boy in years, called on every saloonkeeper at the Soo that morning. "I can't stop you from selling whisky to my canal gangs," Harvey said, "but if you turn another canaller outside when he's had too much to drink, there won't be sawdust left to mark this place of yours!"

The boy who had once organized a Cold Water Army was man-sized now, and he spoke a language the bartenders understood. They took his threat at face value. There were no more Snowmen or Ice Statues of human beings found on sub-zero mornings at the Soo, but the pitiless winter continued to slow up work.

Harvey tried to make up for lost time by working himself at all hours. The canal gangs claimed he never slept. They said that on the coldest nights he could be seen silhouetted against the pines along the canal right-of-way, making instrument calculations, while the Northern Lights blazed and crackled and wheeled like frozen rainbows.

"Young Mister Big could dig this ditch all by his lonesome," the canal gangs used to joke, "but he keeps us around for company!"

As the winter deepened, Colonel Canfield, the government engineer, communicated with Harvey only through his assistant, Major Glenn, a younger man whom Harvey liked.

The Colonel sulked and brooded. He was responsible for the official canal survey and he charted the waters at the Lake Superior pier entrance of the canal.

When, one day in the dead of winter, Major Glenn handed Harvey the complete charts, it caught the young General by surprise.

"I don't understand how he finished all this so fast," he remarked thoughtfully. "The canal survey is one thing. After all, Mr. Nichols and I laid all the ground work for that job, but we've never investigated the waters at the Lake Superior entrance of the canal. It's a mystery to me how the Colonel did it in such a hurry, and in this kind of weather, but give him my compliments."

Major Glenn smiled. "The Colonel is in no mood to receive anything from you — even compliments."

Harvey answered the Major's smile with a boyish grin. "I'm sorry we can't get along, but he thinks I'm too big for my britches and I think he's an old fogey fifty years behind the times. Do you certify these charts as accurate, Major Glenn?"

The Major nodded. "I'm convinced of it. I didn't make the soundings myself, but you don't need to worry about the Colonel taking out his dislike of you on the canal. He's an officer and a gentleman."

After the Major left, Harvey spread the charts out on his desk. He was glad to see that Colonel Canfield's soundings at the Lake Superior entrance of the canal showed

nothing but sand, easy to remove in the closing days of
the canal contract when the waters of the big lake would
be released to flow into the ditch and pave it for fleets of
the future.

Then, frowning at the charts, Harvey had a moment of
foreboding. Major Glenn had said Colonel Canfield was an
officer and a gentleman, but even an officer and a gentleman could make mistakes!

There were incompetent men in the army as well as anywhere else. The Colonel was old-fashioned. He had proved
himself a skimper, and young Harvey hated anything that
came close to skimping when it concerned his pride and
joy, the canal.

Suddenly, a commotion outside drove all thoughts of the
Colonel from Harvey's mind, and he never questioned the
charts again — until it was too late.

10

Work or Starve

Now he scratched a peephole in the frosted window pane to see what the commotion was all about, and then he bolted outside in his shirt sleeves.

It was one of the few pleasant winter days that the Soo enjoyed, and the canal gangs — at ten o'clock in the morning — were skylarking out of the ditch as if the noon whistle had blown.

They scrambled up the sloping sides of the canal, yelling like schoolboys released for a holiday, and headed for town.

In vain young Harvey tried to stop them. He wasted his breath, ordering them back to work. They laughed at him. They said they were sick and tired of working. They were going to have a little fun for a change.

John Tallman Whiting and Mr. Nichols, the old Erie Canal engineer, gathered around Harvey with various construction foremen and members of the commissary. "No use trying to stop them," Mr. Nichols said. "The anti-canal crowd has been encouraging them to quit, and slipping them a jug of whiskey now and then on the sly."

The older men filed gravely into the office and looked at the young man behind the desk.

"This is going to be a tough strike to handle." said Lake Superior's John Tallman Whiting, after several suggestions were discussed and rejected. "The men haven't asked for more money. They're comfortably housed, and fixed with insurance. They've got a fine hospital. We do everything to make working conditions pleasant. They couldn't ask for better food, and — "

Harvey jumped to his feet. "Stop right there!" he exclaimed. "I've got the answer!"

While the canal gangs went on their spree, snake-dancing and parading through town, Harvey and his commissary department hauled all the food from the warehouses and shanties along the cut and hid it far from camp.

Not a crust of bread, not a sliver of meat, not a tea leaf, was left at the diggings. The deep woods had swallowed a whole winter's food supplies.

Meanwhile, the canal gangs had a rollicking time. But sundown found them hungry and they came back to their shanties, expecting the heaping bowls of potatoes and cabbage and beans with molasses, and the great platters of steak and whitefish, and the steaming pitchers of black tea.

But the shanties were empty, the tables were bare, and a scowling guard armed with a shillelagh stood at every doorway and pointed to a sign that said: NO WORK, NO GRUB!

With their stomachs growling, the canal gangs marched up to Canal Headquarters only to find the same sign staring back at them.

Harvey came out to meet their threats of violence. "Fighting will just make you hungrier," he said with his boyish grin, and then his voice rapped out. "Listen, men! You've had your little joke. I know the anti-canal crowd was behind it. They've used you for weapons against me. You were fools to listen to them. They can't feed you. The whole Soo doesn't have enough food on hand to feed you through the rest of the winter."

His grin flashed out for a moment, but the sting remained in his voice. "You're going to be punished. I'm sending you to bed without your suppers! Promise to behave and you'll get your breakfasts. Take your choice. This job is too important for boys. I only want men working for me. And if you don't work, you won't eat!"

The men got up so early the next morning to eat their breakfasts that they were on the job long before dawn!

Thanks to a young man's natural appetite and sweet tooth, Harvey always had hired the best cooks on the Lakes. Two of his cooks were famous on the Lakes — as famous as any chef in New York or New Orleans. All day long the canal gangs dreamed of eating the delectable hash prepared by Michael Phelan's Widow, and their mouths watered for the fabulous doughnuts that were Mrs. Porter's specialty.

The two cooks were partly responsible for Harvey's success. As was said of Napoleon's armies, the Soo Canal traveled on its stomach. There was never another strike on the Big Ditch.

But the long winter still had another blow in store for Harvey. Each week the *Soo Sentinel* came out with an uncomplimentary editorial or news story about the General Agent and his canal.

Harvey paid little attention, trusting in the old jingle that "sticks and stones might break his bones but names would never hurt him."

However, each time the Ojibway mailman shuffled down the snowshoe Pike, he carried copies of the *Sentinel* addressed to every director of the Canal Company, to metropolitan newspapers, and even to Harvey's parents!

Late in winter the General Agent opened a letter from his employers in St. Johnsbury, Vermont. He read the message, first in anger, then in alarm.

A number of canal directors were almost ready to back out of the canal contract.

Discouraged by the *Sentinel's* false reports, they were afraid of throwing good money after bad. They said the contract to complete the canal had only a little more than a year to go.

According to the *Soo Sentinel*, the canal could not possibly be finished within that time. The deadline would never be met.

The contractors would forfeit all the money and effort spent.

When Harvey finished reading the letter, he called for John Tallman Whiting and showed him the bad news.

Forgetting that only a year or so ago he had called himself a Vermonter, Harvey said: "These Easterners don't understand that we're building the greatest canal in the world. They've believed all the newspaper lies. They're scared of losing their cry-baby dollars. Somebody's got to go back there and put some courage into them, the kind of courage we've already put into the Soo Canal. I wish I could go, but I can't leave the job. How about it, John?"

11

Snowshoe Trek

That same day, John Whiting — whose middle name wasn't Tallman for nothing — started down the Snowshoe Pike. It was sixty frozen miles to Mackinac Island, three hundred more miles through the pine barrens to Saginaw, five days and four nights on webbed shoes.

Whiting got his first real sleep on the stage between Saginaw and Detroit where he boarded a train East.

Following Harvey's orders, he went to Syracuse and Albany, New York, and to St. Johnsbury, Vermont, visiting members of the Canal Company and encouraging them to continue the contract.

He was given some hard questions to answer. Young Harvey, brashly confident, had told the Fairbanks Brothers that the canal would cost less than five hundred thousand dollars, but he already had spent that much and he wasn't even half finished!

"Well, yes," Whiting admitted, "but you wouldn't want him to skimp on the Soo Canal, would you? Don't worry, you'll get your money back, and plenty more."

But they *were* worried about getting their money back. Answer this! They could have bought any amount of Michigan lands for ninety cents an acre.

At the present rate of construction, the way young Harvey was spending money, the lands they were to get for building the canal would cost more than a dollar an acre.

In other words, they were paying more than the market price for something they might not even get!

If the canal wasn't finished on time, the lands were forfeit. They wouldn't get paid a red cent!

"Don't worry," Whiting said again. "Harvey will meet the deadline."

Suppose he did, they asked, would the lands he had selected be worth their investment risk?

Whiting shrugged. "The Soo Canal's going to open up a new world of Michigan and Wisconsin and Minnesota iron ore, and western timber and copper and wheat."

They replied, maybe so, but had Harvey picked the right lands?

"Sure," replied Whiting easily. "You bet!"

That's the trouble, the directors said, we *are* betting, we're gambling on one man's judgment, and he's a very young man!

Only time would tell that Harvey's land lists included some of the richest stands of timber in Michigan, mining fields that were to produce ten percent of Michigan's iron ore output, and the fabulous copper king, Calumet & Hecla, destined to yield more than one hundred and sixty million dollars in dividends!

Old Man History was laughing up his sleeve at the nervousness of the Canal Company directors. In his Midas-touch tour of the Iron and Copper Country of Lake Superior, the man they considered too young for the job had put his finger on greater natural resources than all of them put together, had discovered in all their long lives!

Twenty-three-year old Charles Harvey's land lists were gilt-edged! The bluest of blue-ribbon stocks and bonds would have to take a back seat to his selections!

But Old Man History chuckled and kept the secret to himself.

At the dead of winter, John Tallman Whiting came back up the Snowshoe Pike with grudging permission from the directors for Harvey to continue the job.

They would send an Investigating Committee to the canal works in June. That committee would make a final decision about the canal — and about young Charles Thompson Harvey!

Time flew on the canal cut. In June, the Investigating Committee came, saw, and was conquered. They saw a river white with sails and black with smoke as schooners and steamboats rushed supplies to young Harvey's hungry mile of big ditch that was racing the clock around the rapids toward Lake Superior.

They saw sixteen hundred men on the job — the Irish with shovels and wheelbarrows, the Scots with stun-hammers on the embankment's limestone blocks, the Swedish carpenters swarming on pier scaffolds, the German roustabouts — and King Strang's mules heehawing at Harvey's enemies.

Every few minutes the Committee jumped nervously as the powder monkeys set off another charge of Delaware blasting power that shook Sault Ste. Marie from the United States to Canada.

The bearded Easterners stayed a whirlwind week and then gave their General Agent an unqualified go-ahead.

Royally entertained at Schoolcraft's one-time residence of Elmwood on the river front, stuffed like Thanksgiving turkeys with the Widow Phelan's hash and Mrs. Porter's doughnuts, they were dumbfounded by the amount of work their young employee had been able to cram into his schedule.

"What flabbergasts me," Director Seymour said, pointing to a new church steeple along the canal cut, "is how you found time to build a place of worship for your men."

Harvey glanced soberly at the sky-lined steeple. "My father is a minister," he said. "When I was twelve years old, I told him that when I grew up I intended to become a famous builder of tunnels and bridges and canals and railroads. But I promised never to break the Sabbath, and never to let my men work on Sunday, no matter what. I told him that one of the first things I built on any construction job of mine would be a church."

"You remember your promise vividly." Director Seymour said in approval.

Harvey's eyes began to dance. "I've got a good reason to remember," he said. "That was the night I had to go without my blueberry pie!"

No sooner had the Investigating Committee gone, than young Harvey bumped into a serious problem.

Major Glenn reported that he and Colonel Canfield had discovered that the waters of Lake Superior were subject to a rise and fall of several feet annually in addition to the changes caused by storms and wind upon the lake during the season of navigation.

This meant they would have to deepen the canal another foot, and the work would be nearly all rock work at an estimated cost of almost one hundred thousand dollars.

"Why didn't you find this out before?" Harvey demanded. "Why now?"

Major Glenn's cheeks reddened, and he stood silent.

"Why won't you answer me?" Harvey insisted. "Because it's one of Colonel Canfield's blunders, isn't it?"

Major Glenn tightened his lips, unwilling to speak against his superior officer. Finally he said, "The Colonel has asked for a leave. He's a sick man. He'll be going to Detroit in a few weeks, as soon as he finishes the coffer dam.'"

Harvey, sorry to hear about the Colonel's ill health, softened his tone. "If the Colonel isn't well," he said, "I'll be glad to lend him the assistance of Mr. Nichols.

Major Glenn shook his head. "No, the coffer dam's the Colonel's project, and he'd think you were trying to take the credit for it if you sent Mr. Nichols around."

Harvey grunted. "I'm relying on that coffer dam," he said briefly. "I hope it doesn't turn out like this other mistake."

Major Glenn reddened again. "By rights," he said, "and I speak as a state engineer, Michigan should stand the extra expense of deepening the canal, but — "

Harvey nodded his understanding. "By the time the state legislature got through debating the issue and appropriating the money, our deadline would be up and the canal would be nowhere."

Major Glenn agreed, but he pointed out that the Canal Company was not obligated by contract to lower the level another foot, and that the original depth might skimp by most years.

Harvey's jaw lengthened. "I don't skimp," he said. "This isn't just the question of a contract between the Canal Company and the State of Michigan. Every man has a contract with himself. It doesn't involve money, but self-respect. I'm taking the responsibility of digging that extra foot, no matter what it costs."

Major Glenn clapped him on the shoulder. "You'll do, son," he said. "This is a big country, but you fit! I reckon the canal gangs picked the right name for you, Young Mister Big!"

12

The Huntsmen's Warning

Sault Ste. Marie was the roof of the United States, and all through June young Harvey drove his ditch across it.

His canal gangs blasted out the extra foot of depth, and on the last day of June, he stood on a dock below the rapids and bossed the unloading of canal gates sidewheeled up the Inland Seas from Pittsburgh.

The next Sunday he took Kate Bingham, the minister's daughter, to church; and it was a sight to see the canal gangs trooping behind them, all dressed up in their Sunday-go-to-meeting best, some with plug hats, and some with brass-headed canes, and some with fancy spats over their rough work shoes.

Afterwards, Kate coaxed him to walk down toward the river. On the way she asked if he thought the anti-canal crowd had given up their ideas of opposing the job since the Investigating Committee had approved of his work.

"They're just playing possum," Harvey said. "Waiting their chance to strike — like rattlesnakes with the warning rattles cut off!"

As they came to the brawling St. Mary's River, the young couple found an old voyageur sitting on his haunches with an ear turned toward the roar and hiss of white water.

"Bojou!" he said in the universal greeting of the North Woods. "I am listening to the Mist People, the Huntsmen. You hear them out there in the rapids? No? It is not strange. Only a few have the gift of hearing. Me, I am one of the gifted, me, Baptiste Beaubien!"

The voyageur crossed himself quickly against evil. "A brigade of canoes rides out there in mid-stream. The

Huntsmen, the Mist People, they ride in all the rapids, they dip their paddles in every patch of white water between here and the mighty St. Lawrence. This is known to all voyaguers. They are out there forever, dipping their paddles upstream, calling to each other, hidden from us by the spray and mist. They tell the future, these Mist People, to those who have the gift of hearing, like me, Baptiste Beaubien!"

Kate Bingham smiled at the wrinkled old man with the red sash wide around his waist and the eagle feather proud in the voyageur's kerchief knotted around his head.

"And what do these Mist People tell you today, M'sieu Beaubien?"

The voyageur kept his ear bent to the sound of the rapids. "They say trouble is coming, trouble is coming so hurry away!"

Harvey, always practical and matter of fact, humored the old man by inquiring, "What kind of trouble? When is it coming?"

The voyageur shrugged and looked out at the mist. *"They* know," he said. "But *only* they know, and they do not tell these answers, even to me, Baptiste Beaubien, who has the great gift of hearing!"

As Harvey walked Kate home, he said: "You don't believe in any such superstitious foolishness, do you?"

Her answer perhaps was a little too quick. "Of course not! But — *he* believes."

Harvey nodded. "That bothers me too. When a man believes something with all his heart, only a fool laughs at him."

Just a few days later, Harvey thought that the voyageur's premonition of trouble really had come true. It was a hot July afternoon. A worker stumbled from his wheelbarrow with a terrible cry and fell flat on the ground, green sick.

An Irishman took one look and hollered the dread word, *cholera.*

"Asiatic cholera, boys, and sudden death for all!"

Harvey leaped from his mouse-colored pony and hurried toward the fallen worker.

The Irishman got in his way, frantically yelling: "Don't touch him, Young Mister Big! Don't touch him, or sure and we'll all be after burying you too, come nightfall!"

"Out of my way, Donahue!" barked Harvey.

The rest of the men shrank back with Donahue as their boss, swallowing hard, picked up the limp body and rushed toward the hospital. He was afraid, but someone had to do it.

Nothing new to the Lakes, cholera had been rampant in the hot weather months for more than twenty years, since the steamer *Henry Clay* had brought it to Detroit and Port Huron with soldiers from the East who were upward bound around the Straits of Mackinac for the Black Hawk War in western Wisconsin.

Cholera stopped the *Henry Clay* before it reached Lake Huron. Death held the helm. None of the soldiers completed the voyage.

The most recent demonstration of cholera's awful power had come when the city of Cincinatti, faced with a house shortage, was struck with the dreadful plague. Almost overnight, the housing shortage was ended. Death emptied half the homes in town.

All the city newspapers on the Great Lakes, from Buffalo to Milwaukee and Chicago, advertised cholera cures, but there was no cure.

So it was welcome news for young Harvey to hear the diagnosis of the doctor at Rapid's Island Hospital. "This man's going to be all right. He just had too much sun today and too much bad whiskey last night.

13

Shooting the Rapids

One of young Harvey's dreams was turned into reality that summer of 1854. He had shaken hands with the only king ever crowned in the United States; now he entertained an American president.

Ex-president Millard Fillmore visited the Soo, inspected the canal, and, along with his attractive twenty-two-year-old daughter, Mary Abigail, stayed at Elmwood as the former traveling salesman's honored guest.

During the same period, a Michigan politician, Kingsley S. Bingham, also became Harvey's guest, and he brought the first news of an unheard-of political party that had just been formed.

"It happened the first week in July," Mr. Bingham told ex-president Fillmore and Harvey. "There were five thousand of us down in Jackson, Michigan. No hall was big enough to hold a convention that size, so we held our meetings and made our speeches in a shady grove of oaks on the outskirts." He chuckled. "Think of it. That may go down in history as the birthplace of a famous party — under the oaks in Jackson, Michigan. Stranger things have happened."

Harvey nodded. "Yes, sir, and what do you call this new party?"

"We left the name blank for Horace Greeley of the *New York Tribune* to fill in," Mr. Bingham explained. "Horace suggested the Republican Party, but most of us are calling ourselves plain Republicans, and I think the single name will stick."

Mr. Bingham also revealed that he was stumping the state and running for governor on the new ticket.

When he took his departure from Elmwood, he shook Harvey's hand genially. "You've treated me like a prince, young fellow. If I'm elected governor, I won't show you any special favors, but if I can put in a kind word for you and your canal, I'll do it."

Harvey smiled. "I may hold you to your promise, governor," he said. "The canal and I may need a kind word from you before we're through."

With Mr. Bingham gone, young Harvey then arranged a treat for Miss Abigail. Her father declined with uplifted hands and a shake of his head. "I'm too old for that kind of thing," he said. "I'll watch from shore, thank you."

So, with two Ojibway guides to handle the paddles and steer them away from dangerous rocks, young Harvey and Mary Abigail stepped into a canoe and went shooting down the rapids.

The white water seemed to lift them up on wings. The canoe whizzed like a Fourth of July rocket. A few breathless moments of high excitement passed as they went through a maelstrom of boiling spray and black rocks that seemed to leap into the canoe's path. Then they shot out of the rapids and began to drift lazily on the placid bosom of the broad St. Mary's River below the falls.

"Now I know how it feels to be a cork in a bottle of Seltzer water," Miss Abigail cried, her cheeks rosy with the thrill of adventure. "We went pop! fizz!"

The aftermath of the Fillmore visit to Elmwood came in a short and stiff conversation between Harvey and Kate Bingham. "You didn't have to pay her so much attention!" the minister's daughter charged.

"I had to be nice to her," Harvey said. "She's the president's daughter."

Kate pouted. "She's still a girl, isn't she?"

Harvey watched her flounce away in a temper and shook his head in bewilderment. It was a lot easier to build a canal than it was to understand a girl, lots easier!"

Presently a broad smile crossed his face. He felt awfully sorry for his friend, King Strang! Polygamy must be some kind of penance!

14

Sawdust and Cannonballs

In July, young Harvey received word that the government engineer, Colonel Canfield, had died in Detroit. He sent flowers and he allowed no one to say a word against the crusty old soldier, although the colonel's pet project, the coffer dam, was found to be a failure.

"He can't talk for himself," Harvey said. "Let's not try to put the blame on anybody. Let's just go ahead with the necessary repairs and do the job right."

Major Glenn and Mr. Nichols, who had learned many a trick on the Erie Canal, doubtfully experimented with ways to repair the poor coffer dam. Twice they tested it, and twice the surging waters of Lake Superior broke through its flimsy stop-gap, threatening to flood the canal and sweep away more than a year's work.

When the older men, including John Tallman Whiting, admitted defeat, even young Harvey's natural optimism was dampened. He wrote to the Board of Directors back East, outlining the situation and enclosing diagrams of the problem.

Post haste came word from the Canal Company officials. They had consulted the best engineering brains in New York, and they were discouraged. The advice of the experts was to junk Colonel Canfield's coffer dam and build a new one.

At Canal Headquarters, young Harvey called an emergency meeting of his most trusted lieutenants — Mr. Nichols, John Tallman Whiting, and Major Glenn. "It would take three months to build a new coffer dam," he told them. "If we spend that much time, we won't be able to meet our deadline. Any suggestions?"

Glum-faced, the three older men stared at one another and shook their heads. "The smart thing," Major Glenn said, "is to request Michigan to extend the contract time."

Harvey groaned. "You're the state engineer. Do you think Michigan would grant us an extension, say from May 19th, 1855 — that's our exact deadline — for an extra three months to August 19th?"

Major Glenn stared hard at his mud-caked boots. "Michigan might allow a few days of grace, but the anti-canal crowd wouldn't permit any real extension of time. They're still hoping, and betting, that you've bitten off more than you can chew. As quick as the ice breaks up in the Lakes next spring, there'll be a stampede of land speculators up here to storm the U. S. Land Office and file claim to all the choice mineral and timber lands on your lists — one minute after you fail to meet your deadline!"

Nichols and Whiting nodded sober agreement.

"Then what can we do?" Harvey asked, appealing in turn to each of these men old enough to be his father. "The Directors are depending on us. We've got to do something!"

John Tallman Whiting, true product of Lake Superior, stood up and stretched until he seemed to fill the room and bulge the walls. "There's a long road between got-to and can-do, son," he drawled. "But there's more than one way to skin a cat. Let's give these engineers a chance to think while we take a walk and clear the cobwebs out of our heads. You never know when an idea's going to hit. Look at Newton and the apple!"

At first, Harvey had little patience with Whiting's suggestion of a thoughtful walk around the Soo. He wanted to be *doing*, not thinking.

But, as they strolled down the canal cut toward the docks below the rapids, he recalled the story of Newton's apple, and how one moment of thoughtful observation had resulted in the theory of gravity.

Reaching the docks, he and Whiting stopped to watch youngsters dive for the big pennies thrown into the water by the steamboat passengers.

Then Harvey's attention was drawn from the laughing tourists and the screaming divers, to a curious sight at the side of the dock. There a boy of about twelve would plunge his hands into a bucket of sawdust, disappear under a rowboat, break water in a moment to reach up on the dock and grab another fistful of sawdust, and then submerge again.

Whiting answered the question in Harvey's open mouth and wide eyes. "The lad has learned an old sailor's trick," he explained. "That rowboat's as leaky as a sieve but he'll have it water-tight in no time. You see, if he got *in* the boat and tried to stuff the sawdust *down* to fill the leaks, he'd be working against the water pressure and not getting anywhere. But he's diving under the boat and just opening his fist to let the sawdust float free. The suction of water toward the holes pulls the sawdust right into them, then the sawdust swells up inside the holes, and — no more leaks! He's letting Nature do most of his work for him, smart lad."

Young Harvey squinted thoughtfully. "We've got to be as smart as that boy," he said. "The trouble with the Colonel's coffer dam is that it was built to stand *against* the water pressure of Lake Superior, and therefore the water pressure forces the leaks. Now if we could only think of some way to repair the coffer dam so the water pressure would be working in our favor and stopping up the leaks — "

His voice trailed away as his mind caught the flash of an idea and then lost it.

As they resumed their walk along the waterfront, he saw Baptiste Beaubien, the wrinkled voyageur, hunkered down with his ear tuned to the Voices of the Rapids. He smiled grimly. Trouble coming, huh? Trouble was here!

The old sailor's trick had reminded Whiting of his own sailing days on the Lakes, and he told a number of stories to which Harvey barely listened until his ears pricked up at the sound of, "and during the Battle of Lake Erie, my father's ship was hit below the water-line by solid shot, and started to sink. The British thought we were whipped, and sent up a cheer, expecting us to strike our flag. But the carpenter's crew had a patch of canvas ready in jigtime, lowered it over the side on a stretcher to cover the cannonball hole, and the pressure of the water that had been pouring *through* the gap plastered the canvas tighter than a drum *across* the gap and stopped the big leak quicker than you could yell Old Glory! Which is one of the reasons why Commodore Perry was able to send his famous message about us meeting the enemy and them belonging to us."

Whiting waved a calloused hand at the stone barges, lumber hookers, supply schooners, and steamboats in the harbor to feed the canal.

"It's a forest of smokestacks and masts out there now," he remarked, "but every boat has to plow a lonesome road across the Lakes. A sailor can't call for help. He has to depend on whatever is handy in a crisis. That's why his seabag is so full of tricks. But his one sure-fire remedy is canvas. Give him enough sailcloth and he can just about fix anything."

Young Harvey was staring at him, his eyes full of sparks. "Fix *anything?*" he echoed.

Whiting's eyes began to shine. "Son," he said, "you bet your life!"

Harvey was already sprinting toward where the nearest schooner was docked. "I'm betting more than my life," he called back over his shoulder. "I'm betting the Soo Canal!"

A twelve-year-old boy fixing the leaks in his rowboat, and an American warship being kept afloat with a patch of canvas during the historic Battle of Lake Erie in the War of 1812 — these were the basic inspirations for the scheme that young Harvey and his right-hand men figured out to repair the late Colonel's coffer dam.

The Soo thought Harvey had taken leave of his senses when it heard that the greenhorn had bought up the spare mainsails of every sailing ship at the Head of Navigation.

The anti-canal crowd came to laugh and hoot at the sight of the husky canal workers sitting cross-legged like tailors on the ground while they stitched furiously at an acre of billowing canvas.

"What's Harvey making now?" they jeered. "He must be going to put up a circus tent to show off himself and the rest of the freaks!"

Even Mr. Nichols, who had been a technical advisor on the Erie Canal before Harvey learned to walk, could hardly keep up with the General Agent's ideas, and followed him around puffing so fast and so hard on his pipe that it looked like a steamboat in an up-river race.

Not in three months, as the Eastern experts had figured, but in three days, Harvey was ready to test his experiment.

With the entire Soo leaning out windows or standing on tip-toe to see, he gave the final instructions that sent carpenters swarming across the top of the coffer dam to nail one end of the huge patchwork canvas high above water level.

Then the rest of the canvas, stretching from one side of the cut to the other, was lowered to the bottom and anchored fast with barge-loads of gravel.

Harvey took a long breath. "Let her go!" he yelled, and gave the signal that released the full force of Lake Superior into the western end of the canal.

The blue water came flowing, surging, against the coffer dam, searching for the weak spots it had found before. But now the more pressure it applied, the tighter it sealed the dam, plastering the great piece of sailcloth into place so securely that not a drop of water spilled into the big ditch.

The anti-canal crowd growled, and waited for a happier day.

Kate Bingham came up and tucked her arm in Harvey's. "Where on earth," she said, "did you ever get such a wonderful idea?"

Harvey laughed like a boy. It would be hard to explain to anyone, let alone a mere girl! "Well, you see, Kate, it started with Newton and the apple. Then I came across a boy with a leaky rowboat and a bucketful of sawdust. Finally I heard about an American warship that was hit below the waterline by a cannonball but refused to sink."

Kate was such a picture of bewilderment that young Harvey laughed all the way to the verandah of the Baptist Mission. "And now you understand everything," he grinned, "how about fixing me a cold glass of raspberry shrub?"

15

Cholera Strikes Camp

Those last days of summer were glad days on the canal, despite the brooding figure of the old voyageur who could be seen every afternoon squatting beside the rapids, listening to the voices of those he called the Mist People, the Hunstmen.

Baptiste Beaubien insisted that the Voices still warned: "Trouble is coming, trouble is coming, so hurry away!"

Harvey never made fun of the voyageur, and a tiny corner of his mind was worried because of the old man's belief in what he heard, but the young General Agent was too busy to pay much attention to anything but work.

In August he increased his canal gangs to more than two thousand men. He worked them hard, but he worked harder than any of them.

They were proud of their boss. They bragged to newcomers on the diggings: "We've got a man-sized boy in charge of this job. He doesn't drink, doesn't smoke, doesn't chew, doesn't swear, and we bet he hasn't kissed Kate Bingham, but don't make any mistakes about our boy. Young Mister Big doesn't have to *act* tough. He *is* tough!"

The canal gangs called the big ditch the Old Lady, and they claimed she ate a man a day. When a newcomer arrived, they yelled: "Here's fresh meat for the Old Lady, and another slave for Young Mister Big!

They pretended to growl because he drove them like slaves for six days a week and then drove them to church on the seventh.

But it could be noticed that they scrubbed their faces so hard each Sunday morning that they almost rubbed off the freckles, and they followed him to church as proud as brand-new fathers, kicking up their heels to show off their stylish gaiters, twirling their brass-knobbed walking sticks, and tipping their plug hats to Ojibway squaws and Soo housewives alike.

So the weeks went by until a blistering day in August when Harvey was at his deck in Canal Headquarters.

The onetime traveling salesman felt that nothing could stop him now from completing the canal by the deadline. He was far ahead of schedule.

In fact he already had ordered an Osgood dredge to be shipped up by steamer from Cleveland, and delivery had been promised on the last boat of the season.

It wouldn't take the dredge long to remove the sandbar marked on Colonel Canfield's chart at the pier entrance to Lake Superior.

Once that was done, the coffer dam could be eliminated and the largest body of fresh water in the world allowed to flow through the big ditch, thus turning it at long last into the Soo Canal, the most important mile on earth, the road of the future, paved with water!

In the midst of such day-dreaming, Harvey was rudely jolted by a shout outside. He hurried to the edge of the cut.

Men with fear etched on their faces stared up at him as he slid down limestone blocks to the bottom of the ditch.

Despite warnings from the canal gangs, he bent over a Swede sick with cramps and convulsions.

Using a fireman's lift, he raised the Swede and started up a ladder. "Too much hot sun and bad whisky again," he said to hearten the men. "Now get back on the job or

I'll have to send you to bed without your suppers as I did once before!"

The joke, poor as it was, reassured the canal gang. They went back to work without another thought of the sick Swede.

But it was different with Harvey. He had a feeling in his bones, and the sense of dread increased as he passed the listening voyageur on his way to the Rapid's Island Hospital.

Hoping against hope, he waited while the Canal Company doctor made a swift examination. "No false alarm this time," the doctor said gravely. "It's Asiatic cholera."

The young General Agent, afraid of the plague but more afraid of not finishing the canal on time, had a talk with the medical man.

"I don't want to do anything wrong, doctor," Harvey said, "but here's how things look to me. If news of the cholera gets out, my whole working force might stampede overnight. Now, nobody can run fast enough to outrace disease and death."

The balding doctor nodded. "Correct, young man. None of us are fast enough to run away from the plague."

Harvey, his face white, continued. "The Canal Company has the only hospital north of Detroit. If we have a real cholera epidemic, the men would be treated better here than anywhere else within hundreds of miles."

The doctor agreed. "But you won't be able to keep them here. They'll run. They'll go crazy with fear. They'll run until they drop, those that already have the disease in them, and they'll die alone and uncared for out in the wilderness."

Young Harvey squared his jaw. "They won't run, because we won't tell them the truth. They may suspect, but we can keep them guessing. Are you with me?"

The doctor gave a short decisive nod. "Yes, this is the best place for them. With proper care we'll be able to save a certain number of those who get sick."

The Swede died in the night, but news of his death never reached camp. He was reported to have stomach trouble caused by bad whisky.

Other men who keeled over on the job were rushed to Rapids Island Hospital by Harvey, Whiting, or Nichols.

Those who died were taken away from the hospital under cover of night and hauled by wagon deep into the woods. There Harvey said a prayer while Whiting and Nichols leaned on their shovels beside newly-dug graves illuminated by the weird glare of pine torches.

As the terrible days passed into September and the ranks of the canal gangs began to grow thin, Harvey mixed up working shifts to keep the men guessing. They finally suspected there was cholera in camp, but they thought it was a light epidemic kept well in control by the Canal Company's fine hospital facilities.

Less than a hundred deserted. Thanks to a young man who had come to the Soo because of a typhoid attack, the canal never missed a full day of work.

"Actually the ratio of cholera deaths in town is much higher than it is on the diggings," the company doctor told Harvey. "That speaks volumes for your food and sanitary conditions."

Harvey's boyish face was pinched with strain. "But we can't go on much longer! I've lost almost one-tenth of my men! When will there be an end to this?"

The doctor took him by the shoulders. "You look as if you hadn't slept since it began, young fellow. It'll end with the first sharp frost, and not before."

The first heavy frost came the third week in September. A few days later the last plague wagon rolled into the woods and the final victims were lowered by torchlight into a common grave.

Harvey made a wooden cross to mark the spot, but he said:

"They don't really need this marker. Their monument will be the Soo Canal."

16

Mrs. Longfellow Scolds

Once the cold snap had ended the cholera epidemic, Harvey raced his canal gangs against the Currier and Ives calendar to finish most of the work on the big ditch before winter slowed progress.

Watching from a window at the Baptist Mission on lazy autumn days, Kate Bingham wistfully watched another window at Elmwood where she could see a familiar head bent over canal reports. Sometimes, long after she went to bed, she would wake up and go to her curtains. No matter what the hour, a flickering oil lamp showed Harvey at his desk.

It was a great clumsy hulk of furniture, this desk, really a table, scarred by almost thirty years of use, since Henry Rowe Schoolcraft, the Indian Agent who had married an Ojibway princess, first had placed it in the home built for his bride.

Young Harvey, sitting at the desk often thought of what this piece of furniture might say, if it could talk.

As he made out his canal reports for the Board of Directors — so many barrels of blasting powder shipped from Delaware, so many heads of mules purchased from King Strang on Big Beaver Island, so much pork brought up from Cincinnati for Steward Norman Day of the Commissary Department, so many total days' labor estimated in his annual accounting for 1854 — Harvey thought of what else had been written at this desk.

Here great treaties had been signed with the Ojibways; here enormous tracts of wilderness had been sold to the American   government by Ottawa and Chippewa chiefs; here the tribes had assembled on the appointed days each year, coming by canoe and trail from all corners of the North Woods, to stand in line and file forward to receive their share of the clinking bags of U. S. coins; here they had come to trade the prize pelts of the season, prime beaver skins and choice mink furs, a king's ransom held lightly in the arms of a breech-clouted warrior.

And here the famous story-tellers of the tribes had come to tell the legends of their people, the folklore of the lake and forest dwellers, to the man who also had a gift of hearing, a gift even more remarkable than the one claimed by the old voyageur Baptiste Beaubien.

The white man Schoolcraft, said the Indians in awe, could take the sound of their voices and scratch it on paper more enduring than birchbark, and then the eyes of the palefaces could take the scratchings off the paper and make it echo in their mouths.

This was a mystery harder to understand than the messages of long-ago Indians on the Pictured Rocks of Lake Superior.

It was a mystery that only Hiawatha could solve, said the Ojibway story-tellers, and they told him about the miraculous hero of their people while Henry Schoolcraft's busy quill scratched the legend down, page after page.

Young Harvey, especially late at night when the oil lamp flickered low and his own sleepy head drooped toward the desk, often thought about these things, and in his imagination he saw the room peopled with great chiefs in feathered head-dresses and bear-claw ornaments.

On the desk someone had left three huge volumes of Indian lore by Mr. Schoolcraft that the government had published in Washington.

Harvey had thumbed through them, but they were for scholars and hard to read. It would take a famous story-teller to make their material popular.

Often he remembered his visit to Professor Longfellow, when he had delivered Mr. Whittier's eagle feather, and how the poet had joked about weighing Mr. Schoolcraft's heavy books on Fairbanks Scales. Many times he wondered, drowsily, if Professor Longfellow had kept up his study of Mr. Schoolcraft's books, or if he had given them up as hopeless. With a sleepy smile he would recall how Professor Longfellow had asked him to pay his respects to the School-craft home, and here he was, living in the house, using it as company headquarters, bending over the same desk where Mr. Schoolcraft had worked, building a canal where Mr. Schoolcraft had busied himself "building" books about the Ojibway legends and customs.

And, while young Charles Harvey "day-dreamed" far in-to the night at Elmwood, a Harvard Professor with twink-ling blue eyes set in a white-bearded Santa Claus face also bent over his desk in faraway Cambridge, Massachusetts. Night after night he pored through copies of the same huge volumes that lay on the desk at Elmwood.

He would dive into one of the books, come out with an idea, smiling in delight, scratch down his idea in two lines of verse, scowl suddenly, change a word here and there, twitch his white brows to show he was pleased with him-self, and dive back into the books again for another hint from Mr. Schoolcraft, all the while turning a deaf ear to Mrs. Longfellow who kept calling him from another room to say it was far past his bedtime.

"It seems to me," Mrs. Longfellow said, finally having invaded his den in exasperation, "it should be high time you were finished with that poem. You've had your nose in those great big books for almost two years. What you see in them I can't for the life of me understand. They look as dull as dishwater! I wouldn't mind, but this den looks as if it had been hit by a paper snowstorm. You won't let me pick up or dust, and it's a disgrace!"

"Yes, dear, you're perfectly right, dear," Professor Longfellow would say absentmindedly, his body in the room but his thoughts fifteen hundred miles away on the iron-throned, copper-crowned Queen of Lakes that he would never see or hear, except through the eyes and ears of the historian and explorer who had built Elmwood.

Mrs. Longfellow often sighed: "It's easier to manage a houseful of children than a poet!" But she always relented to give him a quick kiss before her nightly ultimatum: "Just two more lines, and then you'll march to bed if I have to take you by the Longfellow ear!"

17

Shipwrecked and Sunk

While Mrs. Longfellow night after night lectured her famous husband for staying up so late, there was no one to lecture young Charles Harvey. Kate Bingham could only watch in disapproval from her own window while he burned the midnight oil at Mr. Schoolcraft's desk, making out his annual reports.

He informed the Board of Directors proudly that the locks, now nearing completion, would be the largest in the world.

They were built not merely for today, he boasted, but for the future. They could accomodate boats almost twice as long as the longest boat on the Great Lakes at the time.

He gave the Directors the exact measurements of the canal. It would be one hundred and twenty feet longer than a mile.

There was only one worry on Harvey's mind, and he didn't pass it along to his employers.

He was concerned about the delivery of the Osgood dredge, as promised, on the last boat of the season. If the dredge arrived, his troubles were over. He could file completion papers early in the spring, a comfortable margin before the deadline.

The Soo Canal would be an accomplished reality!

But he had a nagging doubt about the Osgood dredge, because the old voyageur, Baptiste Beaubien, still could be seen on mild days with his ear turned to the rapids. Once he called Harvey over towards himself, beckoning with a gnarled finger twisted as a hemlock limb.

"I tell you what the Mist People, the Hunstmen, say because you do not laugh at what I hear. They say an ancient North Woods proverb: *Indian Summer — Squaw Winter!*"

Harvey looked blank. "What does that mean?"

The voyageur grunted. "Means many things. Too much fine weather, soon comes bad storms. Too much good news, soon comes bad luck."

So Harvey worried about the arrival of the Osgood dredge.

He did not believe in the Mist People, no more than he believed in ghosts, but he was a little afraid of both of them!

Then, finally, the last boat of the season reached the Soo, and Harvey sprinted for the dock at the foot of the rapids, his heart in his throat.

Suddenly he let loose a yell of joy. There she was, new and shiny, right on deck!

He bossed the unloading, and then hired one of the portage railroads to carry it around the rapids.

He himself sat on the dredge, behind the team of King Strang mules that was pulling the freight car. One of Mr. Whittier's verses leaped into his mind:

> He's whistling round St. Mary's Falls
> Upon his loaded train;
> He's leaving on the Pictured Rocks
> His fresh tobacco stain.

Ship passage to the Pictured Rocks would be possible as soon as the Soo Canal was finished, and meanwhile he was really whistling around St. Mary's Falls! It was a triumphal progress from the edge of Fort Brady, up Water Street through the middle of town, then curving at the sawmill to Portage Road that went to the dock at the head of the rapids.

Here he ordered the dredge put aboard a barge that was towed to the pier entrance at the Lake Superior end of the canal.

On the barge with him at this memorable moment were John Tallman Whiting and the two engineers, Major Glenn and Mr. Nichols.

Under his arm, young Harvey carried 'the charts that Colonel Canfield had made in his government survey. Now he unrolled one of them in the brisk air of early November and studied the directions.

"Let go the anchor!" he called over a certain spot as he cast loost from the tugboat.

A cold sun looked down on the scene, and the barge tossed on the dark, ruffled water.

Engineer Nichols hurled a sounding lead alongside in several places, each time drawing it up with a puzzled frown after touching bottom. His calloused finger traced the chart and he nodded doubtfully.

"We're over the right place and the official chart says it's a sandbar, so it must be me that's wrong," he muttered, "but it's the hardest sandbar I ever took soundings on!"

A chill that had nothing to do with the weather crawled up young Harvey's spine.

"Bring up the first bucket," he told Whiting.

With the donkey engine roaring, the Osgood dredge was brought into action. The long scoop was lowered into the water until it scraped on bottom.

Whiting applied pressure, scowled, changed the position of the scoop, applied pressure again. The donkey engine squealed under the strain.

Abruptly, Whiting turned off the motor. The silence after the roar was a thunderclap. "No use kidding ourselves," he told a white-lipped Harvey. "I don't care what the chart says or how official it is. There's no sandbar down there. It's a rock ledge! Big enough to shipwreck any boat on the lakes — and to sink the Soo Canal!"

18

Barefoot on Ice

Several hours later, four men — Harvey, Whiting, Nichols, Glenn — filed into Canal Headquarters as if they were pallbearers at a funeral.

This was not another emergency; this was final defeat!

They had taken complete and accurate soundings. Their new chart showed them the full extent of the disaster.

Instead of a sandbar easy to remove, they were confronted by a reef or ledge of solid rock tapering from one inch to three feet in thickness and extending over an area of three hundred feet long and one hundred feet wide.

With such a rock ledge at its Lake Superior pier entrance, the Soo Canal would be useless. No average-sized ship could enter or leave without tearing out its bottom on the reef.

Harvey slumped behind his desk. The three older men showed equal dejection. None of them uttered any false hopes and none of them made any accusations against Colonel Canfield.

It was useless to inquire how the error had come to be on the official chart. Had the state engineer been malicious or incompetent or so sick that he had been unable to perform his duties?

A dead man could not speak in his own defense, and, whatever the true answer, the hard fact remained the same: there was a rock ledge where a sandbar had been indicated. Nothing could change that.

"Sorry, son," Mr. Nichols said. "Seems like old hands ought to be able to offer some encouragement, but the only thing that can save the big ditch now is an extension of time. To get that rock ledge, we'd have to build another coffer dam to hold back the water while we blasted a safe channel for navigation."

John Tallman Whiting gave a nod of grim agreement. "We need at least a six-month extension of time beyond May 19th, and there's no way out of the fix, is there, Major?"

Major Glenn shook his head. "No, and this is just what the anti-canal crowd and the land speculators have been waiting for. I'm afraid this is the finish."

As if they were tiptoeing out of a sick room, the older men left Canal Headquarters.

Young Harvey had to face the most unpleasant moment of his life. It was up to him to notify the Directors of the St. Mary's Falls Ship Canal Company that their General Agent had failed. He offered no alibis. He simply enclosed the new chart in his report so that the seriousness of the problem could be seen at a glance.

He presented the verdict of Mr. Nichols, and said there were no other solutions to forward.

In closing, he told his employers that he would await instructions.

The final line of his report showed how much of the bounce had been taken from him.

Always in the past he had gone ahead without waiting for anyone to tell him what to do. Now he wanted instructions.

The canal gangs were quick to notice the change in the man-sized boy whom they had nicknamed Young Mister Big. They said he was down in the dumps and eating humble pie, but they predicted that he'd be himself again in no

time.   Young Mister Big would figure out a way to beat
that rock ledge!

However, a bleak November passed into a cheerless De-
cember, and January marked the happiest New Year on
record at the Soo — for the anti-canal crowd.

The weekly *Sentinel* long since had told the world in scare
headlines about the rock ledge.   Each time the Ojibway
mailman shuffled down the Snowshoe Pike, he carried
copies of the paper to the Michigan Legislature in Lansing,
to the large Eastern dailies, to Harvey's parents, to the
Directors of the Canal Company.   The *Sentinel* gleefully
copied the bad news that came back by way of the Ojibway
mailman.

"Latest despatches from New York," reported the *Sentinel,* "show that stock in the Canal Company has taken
another nosedive.   Our correspondent in Lansing advises
us that the State of Michigan will not grant an extension
of time beyond the contract deadline, and that the lists of
lands will be thrown open to public sale one minute after
midnight on May 20th, next.   This editor freely offers the
following advice to future canal companies:

NEVER HIRE A BOY TO DO A MAN'S JOB!!!

Those were the days when young Charles Harvey stepped
small around the diggings.

He gave routine orders to the gangs in the cut, and he
saw to it that frost-nipped ears and noses were rubbed to
rosy life again with snow, but the buoyant optimism of
youth had gone out of his step.

He ducked around corners to avoid meeting Kate Bingham.   He didn't want pity from any girl!

The knowledge that he had failed made him avoid company.   It was common gossip at the Soo that his employers
would go bankrupt in the spring when they forfeited the
seven hundred and fifty thousand acres of timber and min-

eral lands that he had picked out as payment for building
the canal.

In Buffalo, in Detroit, in Cleveland, in Milwaukee, in
Chicago, in every port on the Inland Seaway, hordes of
land speculators already had booked steamboat passage for
the U. S. Land Office at the Soo as quick as the spring thaw
unlocked the icebound Lakes for navigation.

Young Charles Harvey, ashamed of his failure, became
a desk engineer. He huddled in Canal Headquarters, and
scratched little holes in the frosted windowpane to look out
at a big world, a world that had proved itself too big for
him.

And finally, the letter he had been expecting — and
dreading — was toted up the Snowshoe Pike by the Ojibway mailman.

It contained his instructions, and his instructions
amounted to a dismissal.

The Board of Directors worded it gently, but — he was
fired!

They had consulted McAlpine and Clark, two of the nation's finest engineers, and they enclosed the engineers' report which agreed with that of Mr. Nichols.

"In our considered opinion," said the experts, "the only
answer to the problem is a new coffer dam, necessitating
another season of construction."

With Major Glenn absent in Lansing to make an official
report on the rock ledge to Michigan's Legislature, Harvey
called in his two remaining dependables and told them
about the Director's letter.

"Clark's a number-one engineer," Mr. Nichols com-
mented. "And McAlpine's so good that he was called in to
advise the Austrian government on the improvement of
the Danube River sea entrance."

Harvey nodded listlessly. "They're taking over in the
spring," he said. "I'm out. The Directors are bringing

them on the first boat up the Lakes to the Soo. They intend to complete the canal in hopes that Michigan will allow an extension of time at the last minute and, if not, they'll fight for the three quarters of a million acres of land through court action."

John Tallman Whiting eased forward. "It's a slim chance, but any chance is worth taking." He stared hard at Harvey. "I know it looks hopeless, but you've still got a chance to do what everybody says can't be done. You may be fired, but they can't take you off the job until they get up here next spring. If you can think up an idea, no matter how crazy it sounds, you've got a working crew that would follow you barefoot on ice clear to Superior City — and that's at the other end of the largest lake in the world, Young Mister Big!"

19

Trouble Shooter

When Mr. Nichols and John Tallman Whiting left Canal Headquarters, Harvey had to blink something from his eye. It was the first time the Lake Superior veteran had called him Young Mister Big to his face, and, coming from that source, it marked a new high in compliments.

But Whiting's was not the only word of encouragement he received that week.

The Ojibway mailman also brought a Lansing newspaper up the Snowshoe Pike, marked *special delivery for Mr. Harvey*, and it came from the executive mansion of Michigan.

Mr. Bingham, the genial guest who had been first to bring word to the Soo of the new Republican party formed under Jackson's oaks in July, was now the Governor.

In memory of his pleasant stay at Elmwood, and in return for Harvey's warmhearted hospitality, he had carried out his promise, not to show any special favors, but to speak a few kind words for the young General Agent and his Soo Canal.

The kind words, spoken several days previously and prominently displayed on the front page of the Lansing newspaper, were contained in Governor Kingsley S. Bingham's inaugural address of January 4, 1855.

Speaking of the canal, and indirectly of its young builder, he had said:

"This noble work of internal improvement, rivaling in its magnitude and the fitness and excellence of its structure the most celebrated works of a similar character in the Old World, has been prosecuted with an energy highly creditable to the able direction under which it has been constructed. A less diligent and energetic management would have been intimidated by the serious obstacles which have interposed to impede the progress of the work; as it is, it will undoubtedly be completed within the time specified by the contract for its construction."

The speech was not easy to memorize because of the long, political jawbreakers, but in a few minutes Harvey knew the hardest words by heart. They came rolling off his tongue as he strode up and down Canal Headquarters with some of the old bounce in his walk.

Certain phrases leaped to his lips and he made wide oratorical gestures as he recited them in a loud voice.

"Noble work rivaling the most celebrated works in the Old World! Prosecuted with an energy highly creditable to the able direction! A less diligent management would have been intimidated by the serious obstacles! It will undoubtedly be completed within the time specified!"   .

At a sudden noise and gust of cold air, he came whirling around, his cheeks scarlet at the thought of the spectacle he must have made of himself to one of his canal workers.

But it was Kate Bingham in the doorway, rosy and breathless from her ride to the canal cut in her father's one-horse sleigh.

"What in the world!" she exclaimed. "Charles Harvey talking to himself!"

For the first time in weeks, Harvey smiled. "I used to be a salesman, remember?" he said. "The first thing a a salesman has to do is sell *himself* on an idea, and the rest is simple. I've been talking myself into the idea of removing that rock ledge and finishing the Soo Canal by the May deadline."

Kate almost lost her muff as she threw up her arms in surprised delight. "Wonderful!" A pause. "But how?"

Harvey shrugged boyishly. "How do I know? I haven't got that far in my talk with myself yet! Now clear out of here. I've got no time for girls." He grinned. "Not even for the prettiest girl between the Soo and Superior City!"

"A fine compliment!" Kate sniffed. "There's nothing but wilderness and ice between here and there, no other girls at all!" And she flounced out, pretending to be insulted.

Young Charles Harvey laughed. It was fun to tease Kate again, after all these weeks of avoiding her. But, after her sleigh whisked and jingled out of sight, he paced the floor, wondering how to live up to his bold speech.

The Governor of Michigan could express the belief that he would finish the canal on time, and John Tallman Whiting and Mr. Nichols and the canal gangs could promise to follow their Young Mister Big, no matter how crazy the scheme, but it was all just talk — unless he came up with a plan of action that had at least a prayer of success.

At his desk he drew sketches and diagrams feverishly, but he crushed the papers in his fist with disgust. Why couldn't he meet the challenge of adversity as other men had done? Why couldn't he invent himself out of trouble?

Look at Judge Burt, the Iron Hunter, who had helped him with the Michigan Legislature. Ordinary compasses went wild in the Iron Country and so, to solve the problem of finding out exactly where he was on surveying expeditions, Judge Burt had invented the reliable solar compass, the instrument that had marked the location of every iron range from Michigan to Minnesota Territory.

But that was only one example. Look at Thaddeus Fairbanks, his own employer. He had originally started a hemp business in Vermont and had been a miserable failure at it. But he started figuring out a better method of weighing the wagonloads of hemp he couldn't sell, and the result was an American product known all around the world — Fairbanks Scales.

If a man had the right kind of stuff in him, trouble and failure always brought it out.

The harder a good ball hit the floor, the higher it bounced!

But the more Harvey tried to think of a way to beat the rock ledge, the more impossible it seemed.

Then, on Sunday, as he was marching his canal gangs to church, he bumped into trouble in the form of his worst enemy, the editor of the *Soo Sentinel*. He was loud-mouthed and full of insults.

There were ladies present and the man was drunk. Harvey could do nothing but endure his abuse until his ears reddened.

"Well, well, well," hooted the editor, staggering slightly, "if it isn't Charles Harvey, the General Agent of the Canal Company, otherwise known as Young Mister Big, the man-sized boy! I hear you've got a trifling problem in the form of a rock ledge, Young Mister Big. You know what I'd do if I was such a man-sized boy as you? Why, I'd solve that problem in two shakes. I'd just dive down to the bottom with a little old hammer in my hand and I'd smash that naughty rock ledge to smithereens without coming up once for air. Yes, sir, I'd take my little old trusty hammer —"

At this point, two husky canal workers took him by the arm and, swinging him a moment, threw him spluttering into a snowbank.

But Harvey barely noticed the by-play. He raised his eyes to the church steeple and then he started yelling as if he suddenly had gone crazy.

"A hammer!" he shouted. "That's the answer! A hammer!"

20

Born to Make History

On Monday morning, when Harvey unfolded his scheme
to John Tallman Whiting and Mr. Nichols, the old Erie
Canal engineer and the swashbuckling Great Lakes sailor
began to humor him as if he were feeble-minded.

"Don't look at me like that!" Harvey said. "It was just
the other day, wasn't it, that I was told I had a working
crew willing to follow me barefoot on ice to Superior City,
if I thought up an idea — no matter how crazy it
sounded?"

Whiting rubbed a set of whiskers stiff as a currycomb
brush. "Well, yes," he admitted doubtfully, "but there's
crazy ideas, and then there's crazier ones, but your idea
takes the prize for the craziest! Alongside it, walking barefoot on ice the whole length of Lake Superior sounds fairly
sensible!"

Mr. Nichols chimed in. "My sentiments exactly. Who-
ever heard of a steam punch on a job like this? In the
first place, we can't make one, and in the second place, it
wouldn't work even if we could. Listen to reason, son.
Winter's got us cut off from the rest of the United States.
We're four hundred miles from the closest machine shop,
and that's by snowshoe trail. Can't you just see the Ojibway mailman staggering up the Pike with what we need?"

Harvey squared his jaw with stubborn resolve. "We'll
make everything we need," he announced decisively. "Are
you both with me or not?"

95

The engineer and the ex-sailor exchanged glances. "We're with you, son," Mr. Nichols spoke for both, "but we're anyways twice as old as you are, and we should have learned better sense, so it looks like we're twice as crazy — which ain't possible!"

The plan, immediately put into action, caused the anti-canal crowd at the Soo to roar with amusement when they saw what they dubbed "Harvey's latest piece of foolishness," but the canal gangs had another name for the project: *Harvey's Hammer!*

Technically, it was a steam punch, and the raw iron to make it came from one of the fabulous Lake Superior iron ranges that old Judge Burt had located with the help of his solar compass.

The brawniest men on the diggings were converted into blacksmiths, and they worked at the forge in relays around the clock.

Seven huge forge bellows were kept blowing at the fire to make it blaze higher and blast the iron white-hot so it could be hammered into shape.

Even a Detroit machine shop would have had trouble making the three-ton punch Harvey counted on to smash the rock ledge.

The little blacksmith shop alongside the canal locks almost blew up in smoke and sparks.

Six days a week — morning, noon, and night — it roared like a forest fire, but the seventh day was still a day of rest.

"You're wasting precious time," Whiting warned. "Let's put the men to work on Sunday too. Losing a whole day of work each week is liable to cost you a canal, son!"

But Harvey stuck to the principle ingrained in him as a boy by his father, the Presbyterian minister of Colchester, Connecticut. He looked back on a forbidden slice of blueberry pie, and on the seventh day of every week, he marched his canal gangs to church. They trooped behind him in forty-below weather, but one Sunday they had to clear a path as high as their heads because a blizzard had raged all night.

But they stood in the vestibule to wash each other's frost-bitten faces with handfuls of snow, and then they plunked down on their knees to pray with young Charles Harvey: "Oh, Lord, bless the work of our hands, and grant that the canal we are building be pleasant in Thy sight."

A good many of them added an extra prayer in less formal language under their breath: "And fix it so Young Mister Big's Hammer works, and the ditch gets done on time, Amen!"

Then they sang hymns until the building shook, drowning out the squeaky organ and the ladies' voices until girls like Kate Bingham had to smile into their hymn books at the thought of how overgrown men were so much like boys.

And that was Sunday at the Soo!

As February's icicle days dropped from Currier & Ives calendar on the wall at Canal Headquarters, Harvey spent little time at his desk.

With the huge iron head of the steam punch coming along pretty well, he cruised the woods with his lumberjacks.

They scoured the wilderness on both the American and Canadian sides of the frozen St. Mary's River, tramping up skidroads and hunting the tall timber until they located a towering white oak that must have been an acorn about the time Columbus sailed to discover a new world.

It stood all alone, except for a six-foot pine nearby.

Young Harvey used an engineering trick to tell its height.

He measured the shadow cast by the small pine in the snow, and then he paced off the shadow of the gargantuan oak.

At that time of day, early in the afternoon, the six-foot pine cast a shadow one pace long, or about a yard. Harvey stepped off twenty yards before he reached the end of the oak's shadow.

So he figured that the white oak stretched one hundred and twenty feet high — from the snow line!

His arms could barely reach half way around its trunk. When the lumberjacks felled the oak, Harvey counted and studied the annual rings. The whole story of the tree's life was written there.

"I had lean years and fat years, as anyone can see," the white oak said. "When I was a young girl of sixty, I managed to live through a forest fire that destroyed most of my relatives and friends in this area. Since then, if you'll notice, I have survived two other forest fires that raged across this opening.

"If you count carefully, you'll see that I am three hundred and ninety years old. I have seen many things in my time — three flags waving over the Soo; French, British, American.

"I was here in the days of the great explorers: Champlain, Cadillac, LaSalle, Joliet, Marquette.

"I have been an Indian Council Tree, and in my shade the great chiefs, Pontiac, Tecumseh, Black Hawk, have held powwow.

"I stood here when Frenchmen, dressed in oriental robes, sailed up the St. Mary's in search of the Northwest Passage to China, expecting to sight the Chinese coast as they rounded every broad curve in the stream.

"I stood here when the Hudson Bay Company came in the paddle and portage days, and I was here when American fur traders went all the way west to Astoria, Oregon, to make John Jacob Astor's fortune.

"Great men have turned to look at me as they passed by: Horace Greely, the editor, on his way to the copper mining camps in Lake Superior; the orator Daniel Webster, the poet William Cullen Bryant, who gave your Quaker friend,

Mr. Whittier, the eagle feather you delivered to Professor Longfellow.

"Many others have turned to look at me as they passed by: Captain Marryat, the boys' writer; and, of course, all the men who blazed the trails and tapped the treasures of the greatest of all lakes — General Cass, Henry Rowe Schoolcraft,, William Austin Burt, young Peter White, and now yourself, Young Mister Big!"

Charles Harvey looked up from reading the autobiography of the great white oak as told by its annual rings.

"Handle this tree with care," he ordered the lumber jacks. "Let's hope it was born to make history on the Soo canal!"

They trimmed off the branches so they could haul the oak's long body over the snow to the nearest skidroad. Then they watered down the trail and, when there was a slick bed of ice beneath, they let the trunk slide and skid to the Soo.

There, Harvey called on his Swedish carpenters to do their part of the job.

"We need a stick thirty feet long and fourteen inches square," he said. "Can you carve it out of her stout heart to make a shaft for the steam punch?"

The Swedes grabbed their tools. "Yup," they replied in their sing-song voices. "By Yumpin' Yimminy, yup!"

That was a week for the Soo to remember.

The anti-canal crowd said Harvey was running around like a chicken with its head cut off, spending money like a sailor on a spree.

They called him a maniac, but they followed his every move with concern.

Suppose there was method in his madness? Suppose his crazy scheme worked?

Too much was at stake to leave anything to chance!

21

Fire in the Night

Young Charles Harvey's strange actions puzzled his friends as well as his enemies.

He bought up every available portage railroad freight car.

"Rip off the wheels and axles," he told his goggle-eyed canal gangs, "and throw the rest in the dump."

Kate Bingham was in the lobby of the Chippewa Hotel the day he purchased a lake steamer from its skipper, and her mouth described a round oh! at the fantastic price he paid.

What could anyone possibly want with a steamboat in the middle of winter?

The entire Soo waited to see, and gasped at the final outcome.

Harvey had his canal gangs chop the big ship from the ice and haul it ashore merely to remove its wrought-iron propeller blades.

The anti-canal crowd hooted and predicted that the General Agent's day of reckoning would come when the Board of Directors reached the Soo in the Spring.

"They won't just fire him," the editor of the *Sentinel* growled. "They'll sue him for throwing their money away. They'll put him behind bars, where he belongs!"

Harvey, at Canal Headquarters, grinned as he went over diagrams with Mr. Nichols and John Tallman Whiting.

"Sounds like the opposition's getting worried," he said.
"Next, we'll bolt those tramcar wheels and axles to the sides
of the steam punch for extra gravity, and we'll make those
propeller blades into a socket for holding the oak shaft to
the metal hammer head."

And so the fabulous steam punch grew.

On the second Saturday in March, the blacksmiths and
the carpenters raced to finish the job before quitting time,
but they didn't quite make it.

At midnight Charles Harvey sent the last shift back to
their shanties.

No work on Sunday!

The next morning the canal gangs followed their young
boss to church as usual, but any observer with eyes could
have noticed the knowing glances and cautious whispers
and sly winks they exchanged with one another behind
Young Mister Big's back!

After the services they trooped back to their shanties
and watched from the windows to make sure that Harvey
took the Fort Brady road to Elmwood.

They posted guards on the road, to warn them if
he should return unexpectedly during the day.

Other guards, or scouts, were stationed on the frozen
river in front of Elmwood. They pretended to be ice fishing, but in reality they were ready to send up warning
smoke signals if Harvey moved from the house.

However, their young boss, as was his custom, stayed at
Elmwood all day, and for the first time on the Soo Canal
the law of the Sabbath was broken!

The carpenters and blacksmiths and every man who
could get a finger into the job, worked at top speed on the
steam punch, Harvey's Hammer, in order to surprise him
with the finished product first thing Monday morning.

The Irishmen said: "Sure, and what Young Mister Big
don't know, will nivir hurt him, and it's us that will be

after having our hides toasted a little in purgatory for this, nivir him!"

Even Mr. Nichols and Whiting were in on the secret because their technical help was necessary for the finishing touches.

Kate Bingham also had been let in on the surprise because it was feared that she might drive her father's one-horse sleigh out to Elmwood and innocently give away the show. Kate had her doubts about the whole idea, but she didn't have the heart to tattle on the men.

So, late Sunday evening, the steam punch was completed, ready for presentation to Young Mister Big in the morning, and the canal gangs went home to their shanties, tired but full of satisfaction at a good deed done with the best of intentions.

Then, in the middle of the night, every house at the Soo was awakened by the wild alarm of church bells sounding the fire call.

Shouts rang out. "Look! It's at the canal! The blacksmith shop is on fire! It's blazing sky high! Look! There goes Harvey's Hammer! Up in smoke!"

Charles Harvey bolted awake at the church-bell clanging, an ominous sound in the night.

He tore into his clothes and, racing to the stable, rode a horse bareback to the scene.

Surging across the snow with him were canal gangs from the shanties, soldiers from Fort Brady, citizens from Sault Ste. Marie with overcoats pulled over their sleeping clothes.

As Harvey yanked his rearing horse to a halt as close as he could to the doomed blacksmith shop, one of the roof timbers crashed in a shower of sparks. The flames licked out and set fire to a nearby tool shed.

A half-hearted bucket line formed, but it was an automatic gesture, the kind of thing people do to keep themselves from having to think about disaster.

Harvey wasted no effort on vain motions. Fists clenched, he watched the crowd draw back from the scorching blast of the flames.

Helpless, he saw the fire light up the canal embankment that dropped sheer into the unfinished locks.

Within a matter of moments, the roof and all but one wall of the blacksmith shop collapsed. An instant later the last wall fell, burying the steam punch under roaring ruins.

Whiting and Mr. Nichols, their faces drawn with despair, came up to put comforting arms around the slumped shoulders of their young boss.

Tough canal workers, tears streaming unashamedly down their weather-beaten cheeks, shuffled forward to tell Young Mister Big how sorry they were that their surprise for him had miscarried.

The Scotch stone masons said it must be the judgment of God against them for breaking the Sabbath.

Harvey wondered if the forge fires had been carelessly banked so that sparks had escaped to start the blaze, or if the anti-canal crowd had sneaked in and put the building to the torch.

It was another of those questions to which the correct answer wasn't important. No matter what, the facts remained the same.

The skies above the Soo were red with fire. Accidental or deliberate, the fire had destroyed his last hope of beating the rock ledge and completing the canal on time.

"Don't take it so hard, son," Whiting squeezed his arm. "You've put up a good fight, with all the odds against you. They'll never be able to say you didn't try."

Harvey turned away. "No, and they'll never be able to say I built the Soo Canal either," he said in a tight voice. "Anyone can *try* to do something. It's the man who goes ahead and does it against all odds — he's the man who counts!"

He pushed through the crowd to be alone with his dark thoughts.

Weaklings always blamed bad luck, never themselves, for their failures. A winner had to make his own luck, his own good breaks, no matter how low he felt.

Charles Harvey told himself that, over and over again, but the steam punch that was to have been his best weapon — there it lay in the blazing wreckage of the blacksmith shop!

And what could he do about it?

22

Wild Sleigh Ride

At dawn, only the blackened chimney of the burned-down blacksmith shop stood out against the skyline along the canal.

But young Harvey had rallied from the first shock to meet the situation.

He barked orders at an Irish crew that was rescuing remains of the steam punch from under smoldering timbers and hot ashes.

When they brought it out, he saw that the sturdy shaft had been charred useless.

He told the Swedish carpenters to start carving another thirty-foot stick from the great length of the white oak still lying safely along the embankment half-buried under snow.

Then, along with Whiting and Nichols, he examined the metal head of the punch.

Under the intense heat of the fire, part of it had melted out of shape, and the entire head would have to be heated and hammered and reformed.

"Putting that striking head into shape again is the problem we've got to lick," he admitted, not very confidently, to Mr. Nichols and Whiting. "We've lost time, perhaps a month in one night, but we can build another blacksmith shop, and we can get along with makeshift tools for the most part. Our main trouble is the seven big forge bellows that were burned up. We can't reshape iron without bellows to blow up a hot fire, and there aren't any more at the Soo."

Mr. Nichols shook his head grimly. "Far as I know, the nearest bellows of the size we need are at Saginaw and Dee-troit. They'd have to be brought up the Snowshoe Pike, and it would take forever."

An old voyageur in the crowd of onlookers stepped forward. "Bojou!" said Baptiste Beaubien in North Woods greeting. "Me, I have the gift of hearing the Mist People, the Huntsmen." His mouth split in a wide grin. "Also I have the gift of hearing what you say about these forge bellows, m'sieu. Take a sled and come with me. We will bring back the seven you require, in as many days."

Harvey asked where they would go, and the old voyageur waved vaguely to the north and the east. "Canada," he said. "Little places with big hearts, portages, steamboat landings, sawmills, fur posts, clearings in the woods."

Charles Harvey wasted no more time with questions. He left instructions with Whiting and Nichols, borrowed the one horse sleigh from Kate Bingham's father, and, with Kate waving from an iceberg near the rapids, he and the old voyageur went jingling down the frozen St. Mary's River, toward Lake Huron.

The speedy cutter zipped past the stone quarries on Drummond Island, its slick runners whisking over the snow and the horse's hoofs beating like a kettledrum on the river ice.

"En avant!" cried Baptiste Beaubien, cracking his whip, and it was full speed ahead as they shot out the North Channel at the mouth of the St. Mary's and entered the vast snowbound and icelocked expanse of Georgian Bay on Lake Huron, where the icebergs were piled up high as church steeples.

To while away the time, the old voyageur taught his young friend a French folk song, and they sang it to the jingle of sleigh bells:

> Oh, les fraise et les framboises,
> Les vins que nous avons bu,
> Et les belles villageoise,
> Nous ne les verrons plus.

"Oh, the pretty village girls, we'll never see them again," translated the voyageur. He glanced slyly at his passenger. "You have a pretty girl in the village of Sault Ste. Marie, no?"

"No!" retorted Harvey, but the reply was too quick and too loud, and his cheeks became as red as if they had been slapped.

The voyageur smiled to himself, and hummed the song. Later, he pointed far ahead to a thin wisp of smoke.

Within an hour they reached their first stop, a steamboat landing where a few houses were huddled together around a general store and a church.

Their arrival was a great event in the village, with the habitants and the French housewives hurrying to salute Baptiste Beaubien on both cheeks in the Gallic style, and children turning cartwheels of joy as Harvey — who had bought out the Soo's supply of candy before he left — hauled presents for each of them from a huge flour bag.

A Santa Claus without a beard, he could have walked away with everything in the village from then on, but when he gave out copies of newspapers that were months old, the habitants were his to command.

Did they have a large forge bellows? Yes? Would they sell it for a fancy price?

Sell it, m'sieu? It was his for the asking! Take it away! A mere bagatelle!

But Harvey clinked twenty dollar gold pieces on the counter of the general store.

If they refused to accept the money for themselves, then take it as a donation for the church.

The habitants nodded approval and toasted the bargain in brandy while he drank a stirrup cup of raspberry shrub.

With the cheers of the village echoing behind them, off he and Baptiste Beaubien went, with a fresh Canadian pony to whisk their sleigh to the next settlement on Georgian Bay.

Their reception, from portage place to fur post to saw-mill landing, was always the same.

The candy and the out-dated newspapers were what counted, the Gallic salutes, the handshakes, the smiles — not the twenty-dollar gold pieces, the so-called double eagles.

Coins were soon spent and forgotten, m'sieu, but a visit from the outside world in the winter, ah, mes amis, said the habitants and the hivernants, that was something to re-member and treasure all one's life!

So, in little more than a week, the young canal builder and the old voyageur zipped back to Sault St. Marie.

On a highway of ice they had crossed a bay on Lake Hu-ron, Georgian Bay, so large that it deserved rank as the sixth Great Lake.

They had dodged the swift cutter through islands thick as mice, and they had steered past mighty Manitoulin, largest of all freshwater islands.

They had covered hundreds of miles across the windy map of March, and they returned with seven pairs of huge forge bellows to blast a fire for the steam punch's striking head.

In their absence, the canal gangs had not been idle. Black smoke already was mushrooming from the chimney of a brand-new blacksmith shop.

Living up to his middle name again, John Tallman Whit-ing had raced on his bear-paw snowshoes to Pendill's Saw-mills in Lake Superior's Whitefish Bay at the mouth of the

Tahquamenon River and, by hook or by crook, he had shuffled back with a pair of bellows to keep the fires hot while Harvey was gone.

Carpenters were swarming the length of the giant white oak, carving the rest of it into proper shape.

With eight pairs of bellows pumping, the forge furnace again raced around the clock — except on Sunday! — to make up for lost time.

Harvey wanted no more surprise parties, either from his loyal canal gangs or from his enemies at the Soo.

He posted watchmen, not only to see that the Sabbath was strictly observed, but also to make sure that no civilian feet stepped across canal property.

All along the cut he put warning signs: TRESS-PASSERS SHOT ON SIGHT! Then in smaller print: *And Prosecuted Next Summer — If Still Alive!*

The canal gangs were spoiling for a fight. They dared anyone in town to look cross-eyed at them. The Irish strolled around the Soo, twirling shillelaghs and hoping for trouble. The canny Scots carried brass knuckles in their pockets. The Swedes and the Germans held head-butting contests to show the world the hardness of their skulls.

Observing these signs of bristling vigilance and zest for battle, the anti-canal crowd stepped softly and carefully, but they walked big with confidence. They were certain of victory.

The *Sentinel's* editor and the owners of the two portage railroads had turned into eager land specluators. They could be seen, on the street and in the taverns, buttonholing prospectors who knew the mining country, and bribing their opinion of the richest lands on Harvey's lists.

Each week the *Sentinel* repeated its old story: The man-sized boy had turned out to be a mere babe in the woods; Harvey was in for a spanking, come May 19th; Young Mister Big would soon get his come-uppance!

In scarehead bulletins splashed across its front page, the *Sentinel* reported:

CANAL COMPANY STOCK DROPS FIFTY PERCENT

FORFEIT OF STATE CONTRACT NOW POSITIVE

STAMPEDE TO UPPER PENINSULA LOOMS
AT START OF NAVIGATION

750,000 ACRES OF CHOICE TIMBER AND MINERAL
LANDS WILL BE THROWN OPEN TO PUBLIC

ENTRY AT U.S. LAND OFFICE
IN SAULT STE. MARIE
ONE MINUTE AFTER UNFINISHED
CANAL'S MAY 19TH
DEADLINE

The bulletins in the *Sentinel* were copied by the metropolitan papers in Detroit, New York, and other large cities. Stock in the Canal Company continued to drop. Confidence in young Charles Harvey hit bottom, *rock* bottom!

23

Spring Artillery

When General Agent Harvey ripped March off the Currier and Ives calendar at Canal Headquarters, he had a moment of panic before he went back to work twice as hard as ever.

There was only a month and nineteen days to go!

In Detroit, the waterfront hotels on Jefferson Street were bulging with land speculators.

In Buffalo, the Board of Directors and the new engineers, McAlpine and Clark, were waiting for the Upper Lakes to be declared open to navigation.

In Cambridge,, Massachusetts, a Harvard professor was drawing near the end of his long poem, while his wife continued to scold him for working so late at night, and for not letting her dust and pick up in that disgraceful den!

In Superior City, at the far end of Lake Superior, in Duluth, Minnesota Territory, the chinook winds began to blow their warm breath against the great ice sheets of Fond du Lac Bay.

The Spring Breakup was at hand!

With artillery salvos, with the thundering crashes of cannon locked wheel-to-wheel in battle, the ice gave way.

Mountains and juggernauts of ice, pushed by the warm winds, moved sluggishly toward the Soo Bottleneck.

Whiting and other oldtimers took one look at the housetop jams of ice in the St. Mary's River and predicted, correctly, that the first boat to reach the Soo would not be able to push up-river until the second week in May.

"Looks like a late season, even for the Soo," Whiting shrugged. "But what can you expect in a country where it's ten months winter and two months poor sledding!"

But the late season suited Harvey. The more time he had the better.

As soon as the Directors arrived, he would be out of a job. McAlpine and Clark would take over. Young Mister Big would be a has-been — worse, a never-was! — at the ripe old age of twenty-five!

But meanwhile, luck and the weather were with him. He had one last chance, and, win or lose, it would be news to the outside world only when the first boat blew for a spring landing.

Because even the Ojibway mailman was out of business!

Spring floods and freshets closed the Snowshoe Pike, suspending all overland mail communications.

Behind a white wall of silence, with the Soo cut off from the rest of the United States, young Charles Harvey drove himself and his men to final victory or defeat.

Only time would tell — the thirty days of April, and nineteen more days in May!

The first week in April, the carpenters and blacksmiths put the finishing touches to the steam punch — three tons of wood and metal that meant all, or nothing.

Mr. Nichols, the old Erie Canal engineer, kept a sharp eye on the way the tremendous oak handle was fitted into the huge iron socket of the hammer head.

There was a nervous pitch in Harvey's voice as he bossed the canal gangs that heaved and grunted and hauled the massive machine from the blacksmith shop to the west end of the big ditch.

He patted and rubbed the mighty bullet-headed business end of the tool that would either smash a rock ledge, or break his heart.

By mid-afternoon, preparations were ready for the test, and the whole Soo was on hand to see the show; lumberjacks, voyageurs, traders, trappers, prospectors, Michael Phelan's Widow in her Queen Anne bonnet, next to an Ojibway squaw with a papoose strapped to her back; a lake captain in his Prince Albert coat rubbing elbows with a buck-skinned coureur du bois; a British remittance man squinting through his monocle, and a Chippewa chief wrapped in a Hudson Bay blanket but standing in stylish Wellington boots and sporting a top hat imported from London.

Kate Bingham waved encouragement from her father's buggy. The anti-canal crowd, now get-rich-quick land speculators, watched with fear and hate in their eyes as they stood on the pier entrance to Lake Superior and gaped at the size of the machine that had been fitted into the towering spile driver on the scow out in the ice-tossed river.

Harvey boomed orders and managed to be in half a dozen places at once.

He helped string guides into the frame of the spile driver; he fixed a system of ropes and pulleys to hitch his punch to the drum of the steam engine operated by John Tallman Whiting; he checked the reels that worked ropes from the scow to the opposite piers so the scow could be held steady or moved by turning the reels; he marked a guage on the thirty-foot shaft of oak to show how deep the punch must be driven through the rock reef to smash out the required depth.

"When the green band slaps the water level," he said, "it's deep enough in that place."

An Irish gang set up a cheer. "Sure, and green's the color that will win every time," they yelled. "There's nothing can stand up against the wearing of the green!"

All the canal gangs broke into a roar as John Tallman Whiting stepped forward on the scow with a long-necked red bottle dandified with wide ribbon and a fancy bow.

While Harvey stared in wide-eyed, open-mouthed surprise at the ceremony, a hush fell on the crowd, and Whiting's voice could be heard on both the American and Canadian shores of the Soo.

"With plain raspberry shrub I christen you Harvey's Hammer," he announced as he broke the bottle across the metal nose of the steam punch. "And you'd better be a *tee-total* success!"

The canal workers along the embankment threw up their hats and hollered. Harvey blushed and grinned like a schoolboy.

Then he called out: "Ready for testing!"

With these words, he grew tense. His muscles knotted. His heart jumped aboard his adam's apple and rode up and down in convulsive swallows.

Except for the thin wail of a baby, the onlookers became as quiet as the pines that stood in the background.

Like a mighty finger, the white oak shaft poised above the water. The steam engine pulsed, guide wires sang, and the reels worked the scow into position.

"Move her a hair," Harvey called. "Move her a split *red* hair!"

The scow shifted over the reef. It was hard to make calculations because of the ruffled water and the float ice.

He glanced at his chart, squinted into the depths, and then his hand flashed the signal: "Let her go!"

Too late he saw that a piece of float ice had helped to fool him. The scow was not over the exact spot.

The steam punch would strike the rock ledge a glancing blow. But there was no calling it back.

All he could do was hope that no damage would result.

Down drove the drillhead, down slammed the shaft. Instead of a solid blow, there was a sickening, splintering sound.

The steam engine raced as if it had suddenly been relieved of weight.

Whiting made savage noises under his breath as he brought up the shaft. It came out of water without the mighty drillhead. It had broken off at the socket!

A funeral sigh swept the canal gangs.

Mr. Nichols sat down wearily and buried his face in his hands. Harvey stared into emptiness.

The land speculators, with nothing to fear any longer, walked back to town with thumbs stuck jauntily in their vests.

"Harvey's Hammer?" they jeered. "Harvey's humbug!"

24

Three Tons of Fist

Kate Bingham, being a girl, cried herself to sleep that night, out of pity for Harvey. But, along with the rest of the Soo, she sprang awake at dawn to a sound that seemed to rip the air and shake the earth.

Plunge! Strike! Hoist!

It made the dishes rattle on the shelves.

Kate ran to her window and looked out with wondering eyes toward the Lake Superior pier entrance.

Harvey's Hammer was in action as if it had never been damaged. It sounded louder and more powerful with every blow struck.

PLUNGE! STRIKE! HOIST!

While Kate had cried herself to sleep, Harvey and his canal gangs had fished and grappled for the metal drillhead lost at the bottom of the freezing-cold waters of the channel.

With pine flares painting the gloomy scene, they had fought all night with the dark waves and the float ice until finally they had dragged the drillhead up onto the embankment.

After that it was a simple job to remove the splintered wood from the socket and re-trim the broken-off end of the shaft.

Then, once again, the shaft was bolted to the drillhead and taken aboard the scow.

At dawn, Harvey tested for the second time, and the Soo awoke with a bang.

Plunge! Strike! Hoist!

The shamrock-green band on the shaft had to be raised two feet because of the repairs, but two green bands were twice as good as one, said the Irish, and the length lost from the shaft made no great matter.

Plunge! Strike! Hoist!

Whist, and there's the first green band, Paddy, me boys!

PLUNGE! STRIKE! HOIST!

Sure, and here's the second, praised be Saint Patrick!

From that morning on, the canal gangs, working three shifts around the clock, kept Harvey's Hammer in constant motion — except on Sunday, never on Sunday, not even if a canal contract went glimmering because of the lost time — as three tons of fist on a twenty-eight foot arm smashed through the wedge of reef at the Lake Superior entrance toward the rock ledge's hard hump.

And while Harvey's Hammer fought to finish its job within the deadline, the Soo saw another necessary milestone reached in canal construction — it was a sight to be remembered and to be told, long years later, to grandchildren!

Housekeepers, hanging up their daily wash of Keeweenaw nips for the shanty boys late one morning in April, were the first to notice the history-making event.

With clothespins in their mouths, they shaded their eyes, then hiked up their skirts and ran toward the diggings.

The rest of the Soo, hearing excited cries, hurried toward the scene or watched from high windows.

A stranger might not have seen anything unusual in what was happening, but Sault Ste. Marie had been watching the big ditch for two long years, and even the boys and girls on their way home from school realized that this was a moment to be remembered all their lives.

It was a homely sight, but they dashed for the embankment to watch King Strang's construction mules, lowered for duty months ago, hoisted out of the cut.

If a newcomer had asked them what they were so excited about, they would have replied scornfully: "Can't you *see?* Young Mister Big doesn't need his mules any more. He's finished the canal locks. Gosh, anybody ought to know *that!*"

In the afternoon of the same day, young Charles Harvey proved the boys and girls had guessed right.

Proud of the moment, but without making any fuss about it, he opened the sluice gates of the coffer dam and let Lake Superior flow into the finished canal prism.

His eyes glowed as a silver mile of water moved between the limestone walls.

He had finally paved his big ditch in the only way a ship canal could be paved. He had macadamized Michigan's all-important mile with sparkling water.

But he could spare no time to celebrate. Nothing counted unless the steam punch beat the rock-ledge!

Plunge! Strike! Hoist!

The days flew across the Currier & Ives calendar at Canal Headquarters.

Harvey's Hammer advanced on a front one hundred feet wide against an enemy one hundred yards long.

Maynineteen-maynineteen-maynineteen! the hours sang ominously as the canal gangs raced time, and an iron fist on a stout arm punched away at a rock reef.

A great test came when the ledge hump showed below.

With Mr. Nichols nursing the steam engine, and Whiting and Harvey working on the reels, the scow was maneuvered directly over three feet of solid rock.

"This is the big one," Harvey said, squinting down, "If she can smash through what's below, then we've got a real fighting chance to win the whole battle."

He paused an instant, glancing up toward the steeple of the church he had built, and then yelled:

"Let 'er go!"

The steam punch thundered into motion.

Plunge! Strike! Hoist!

The first shamrock gauge on the great oak shaft reached water level.

Plunge! Strike! Hoist!

The second shamrock gauge showed one more foot to go.

PLUNGE! STRIKE! HOIST!

"Saint Patrick's color!" bragged the Irish, as the second shamrock gauge slapped the water.

"Sure, and you can't beat the wearing of the green!"

Night and day thereafter, the steam punch battered the thickest portion of Lake Superior's reef.

She wore thin from her three tons, and as she lost weight she picked up scars, but she drove and drilled through the worst sections of the rock ledge.

Harvey's Hammer had the spirit of her young namesake. There was no stopping her, short of destruction.

The most critical test came the last week of April.

Harvey had delayed the showdown, but now he had to know.

His steam punch could smash a rock reef, but the vital question remained: Was it breaking the reef into small enough fragments for the Osgood dredge to remove?

"Scared, son?" Whiting asked, when the decisive moment was at hand. "You look a little pale around the gills."

Harvey worked the dredge barge into position. "I even *feel* pale," he admitted. "But let's get it over with, one way or another." His voice cracked. "Lower the scoop!"

With Whiting operating the levers on the dredge and Mr. Nichols wheedling the engine, there was nothing for Harvey to do but wait.

He sat down, his knees knocking. He watched while, three times, the scoop came up empty. Then, heart in mouth, he gambled everything on one throw.

"Go full steam! Bring up a scoopful of rock or bust the dredge trying!"

The canal gangs held their breath.

Mr. Nichols gulped.

Whiting, tense as a bear trap, fussed with levers. He drew back the scoop to its limit, scraped bottom, then applied the last reserve of holding power.

Squealing and trembling, the dredge almost shook to pieces. The barge itself rocked under the strain. Slowly the scoop approached the surface.

Harvey's eyes said prayers that were suddenly answered. The scoop came out of water. It was full to the brim with broken stones, and not a lump of it larger than a man's fist.

It was Whiting who said the words that sent the canal gangs skylarking and whooping in delirious victory celebration along the embankment.

"Why, it's nothing but rock candy," he said. "Little old pieces of rock candy. And it looks like those land speculators will get an awful big toothache eating it!"

25

Real Rock Candy

Two weeks later, on May 10, 1855, the St. Mary's River, in one of the latest seasons on record, finally opened to navigation, and the ships that had been waiting out in Lake Huron went full-steam toward the Soo, their docks mobbed with land speculators hurrying to file claims on the timber and iron and copper locations that the Canal Company would forfeit for failure to meet the deadline within the next nine days.

In the main salon of the leading steamer, the Canal Directors — along with their new team of famous engineers, McAlpine and Clark — were holding another grave conference.

They were not the kind to nurse false hopes, these bearded business men such as President Corning of the New York Central Railroad, Brooks of the Michigan Central, and Erastus Fairbanks, executive head of the world-renowned Scales Company in St. Johnsbury, Vermont.

It was true that the State of Michigan had reached no final decision on their request for a time extension, but the political pressure being brought to bear against them by the Land Lobby in Lansing was overwhelming.

At the very best, the Board of Directors looked forward to a long legal struggle, with the binding terms of the contract square against their case in court.

"Unless, of course, young Harvey's gone ahead and rigged up something that might — " Erastus Fairbanks let his words trail away in embarrassment and ducked his gray head in apology to the great engineers. "You still don't think it's remotely possible? Not even the ghost of a chance, gentlemen?"

McAlpine and Clark looked tolerantly at the oldest of the three Fairbanks brothers. They shook their heads firmly. Not a chance!

"Well, I'm sure you're right," sighed Erastus Fairbanks, "and I hate to keep bringing up this subject all the time, but, you see, my brother Thad sort of figured young Harvey might think up an idea and — " His voice lost momentum again.

"Nonsense!" President Corning interrupted irritably. "Besides, what does your brother know about canals?"

Erastus Fairbanks spread his hands. "Nothing, nothing at all," he admitted. "But Thad didn't know *boo* about platform scales either," he added mildly. "Not until he went ahead and *invented* them — "

The steamer blew for a landing at the foot of the rapids, and the long-faced Directors filed down a companion-way to the gangplank where they were jostled in the rush of land speculators eager to get ashore.

Young Charles Harvey, poker-faced and non-commital, met his employers at the dock and nodded stiffly to McAlpine and Clark.

"This way, gentlemen," he said. "Carriages are ready to take us to the rock reef."

He helped the three most important Directors — Corning, Fairbanks, and Brooks — into the same carriage with himself and the eastern engineers.

Whips cracked and the jouncing buggies began to drive along the canal cut toward the Lake Superior pier entrance more than a mile away.

Harvey glanced at the silver lining to all his dark clouds — the silver lining of water that sparkled in the sun along the big ditch.

He could not resist the temptation to ask McAlpine and Clark: "Do you still think, now you've had more time to consider, that it will be necessary to build another coffer dam and spend an extra season of construction in order to remove the rock ledge?"

The famous engineers looked down their long noses at this self-taught whippersnapper who dared to suggest that they might have been wrong in their original opinion.

He needed taking down a peg. His manner was too jaunty for a failure about to be replaced on the job by men with the proper experience and credentials.

"Mr. Harvey," they said, stiff in attitude and answer, "we are prepared to uphold our judgment against any corps of engineers in the world!"

Harvey nodded, as if properly squelched, but there was something in his eyes that made Erastus Fairbanks look sharply at him and then turn his thatched brows toward the water dancing in the canal.

The buggies reached the Lake Superior entrance, whereupon the Board of Directors and their new engineers began to climb out onto the pier to inspect the submerged obstruction.

"Don't bother yourselves, gentlemen," Harvey called, his voice leaping at the little joke he had played and the wonderful surprise he had in store for them all.

"Stay in your seats. I've arranged for us to view the situation comfortably from here." He pointed to the hills of broken stone rising from the opposite bank, then he crowed: "There's your rock ledge! We call it rock candy! And it's mighty hard for some people to swallow!"

When Harvey broke the news, John Tallman Whiting was on hand to see the effect on the faces of the Directors and their engineers.

"For about ten minutes, their eyes were the biggest part of them," he remarked later. "And their mouths flew open so wide that they looked like traps to catch all the bugs at the Soo!"

The Board of Directors, recovering from joyful shock, overwhelmed Charles Harvey with praise, almost shaking his arm from its socket, but it was Erastus Fairbanks who went up to the youngster he and his brothers had hired originally as a traveling salesman and who now paid him the compliment that pleased him best of all.

"Brother Thad would admire to see this," he beamed. "I don't hardly think even my brother Thaddeus could have invented himself out of trouble a speck better!"

The Board of Directors called a meeting to order right at the pier entrance and gave their young General Agent a vote of thanks on the spot.

There was no more thought of replacing a self-made engineer with Eastern experts.

The tour of inspection was a victory march.

Mr. Nichols pointed out the steam punch still pounding away, trimming the edges of the channel.

They stood thunderstruck while Harvey's Hammer sledged blows of more than thirty tons to the square inch on rock twelve feet below the surface.

McAlpine and Clark seemed to have shrunk in size. They hung on Harvey's every word. It was yes, Mr. Harvey, yes, indeed, sir, and it was Charles Thompson Harvey, Boss of the Works! If they had known his nickname, they would have called him Young Mister Big!

In town, the boatloads of land specuators heard disquieting rumors and swarmed toward the *Soo Sentinel* for information.

A sour-faced editor told them the truth.

"But what happened?" they asked, and John Tallman Whiting came strolling up, happy to tell them.

"Harvey happened!" he laughed in their faces. "Young Mister Big measured true to size! You'd better book return passage to wherever you came from, because you won't find easy pickings here!"

Overnight, the disappointed land speculators vanished.

Even the crestfallen editor soon sold out to an honest publisher and skipped out of town, leaving bad debts behind.

Every day Sault Ste. Marie bustled and bulged with more arrivals from below. Government inspectors and state engineers swarmed along the canal to check the two great locks and the waterway that by-passed the rapids.

Celebrities poured into town as Governor Bingham sent out calls for Michigan's favorite sons — the Iron Hunters, the Trail Blazers, the Legend Makers, who had earned the historic honor of berths aboard the first ship to sail from the Lower Lakes into Lake Superior.

Every ship owner and captain on the Lakes — from Montreal to Mackinac to Milwaukee — fought for the privilege of taking his boat through as the lead vessel.

Sail argued with steam for the right of first passage.

There were riots at every port of call on the Inland Seaway as sailors backed up their opinions with their fists.

A whole parade of paddlewheelers, propellers, and windjammers beelined for the Soo to lay claim to the greatest honor the Lakes would ever be able to bestow on a ship.

With the excitement mounting by the hour, Governor Bingham announced that young Charles Harvey was the one man who had the right to make the choice.

It was another knotty problem for Harvey to solve.

Hundreds of boats had helped in building the Soo Canal: lumber hookers from Lake Huron; limestone schooners from Lake Erie; sidewheelers and sternwheelers that had brought up the canal locks and gates from Pittsburgh; swift sloops that had skimmed through the Welland Canal from Lake Ontario with dangerous kegs of Delaware blasting powder; Lake Michigan propellers bound up from Chicago with prairie grain and Cincinnati pork for Steward Norman Day's Commissary Department; errand-running Mackinaw boats and mail packets; Captain McCargo's *Minong* and old Cap Sparhawk's *Prairie Dew* and other passenger ships that carried the immigrants snatched by Harvey's agents as they landed in Boston, New York, or Philadelphia.

From the fleet of ships that had served the Soo Canal, which boat should be singled out above all the others?

The decision meant a great deal. The chosen ship would have a special place in history books.

Harvey wrestled for the proper answer. Meanwhile, the Soo Canal officially passed inspection by Michigan's engineers well within the contract deadline. Major Glenn and a Canal Director filed the necessary papers of completion in Lansing on May 24th, 1855. Governor Bingham proclaimed June 18 as the date for first passage through the Soo Canal.

June 18 — two days after Young Mister Big's twenty-sixth birthday!

26

Hiawatha's Birthplace

A week before the historic event, Charles Harvey was still struggling to select the honored boat when Kate Bingham came running up the path to Elmwood, waving a package in her hand.

He went outside to see the reason for her hurry.

"It's right off the boat from Buffalo," she said indicating the package, "and it looked so mysterious that I promised to deliver it right away. Open it, quick! I'm dying of curiosity. See, it isn't even addressed to you, just—'Elmwood, Where Henry Rowe Schoolcraft Recorded The Folklore Of The Ojibways, Sault Ste. Marie, Michigan.' — Hurry, slowpoke! If you don't open it this minute, I will!"

Harvey frowned at the package. It was about the size of a book and had been sent from Cambridge, Massachusetts.

He stared blankly for a moment. Then a flash of inspiration told him the truth. He had a good idea of what was inside the package, and who had sent it, and why. But he wanted to tease Kate.

He opened the package with exasperating slowness — to her — and then scowled at the contents. "Why, it's nothing but a lot of poetry," he said in pretended disappointment.

"Nothing!" Kate cried, snatching it from him. "It's an advance copy of a whole new book by Henry Wadsworth Longfellow, that's all! *The Song of Hiawatha!*"

Harvey remembered the eagle feather he had delivered from Mr. Whittier to Professor Longfellow at Cambridge;

he remembered the works of Schoolcraft on the poet's desk; he vividly remembered his parting words, "Please give my respects to Mr. Schoolcraft's home when you reach the St. Mary's"; but he wanted to tease Kate, so he put on a mask of bewilderment and asked: "But why should this song or poem or whatever it is be sent *here* to Elmwood of all places?"

Kate took his hand and began to pull him toward a shady place under one of the umbrella-shaped elms down by the river.

"We've got the whole afternoon ahead of us," she said. "I'll read the poem to you, and maybe we'll find out." She coaxed him prettily. "Please, Young Mister Big!"

Lazy for once, Harvey spread his coat for Kate on the grass and settled down with the trunk of a tree for his backrest.

Dreamily he watched the busy sails and paddlewheels of the Great Lakes bustling up and down the St. Mary's. He caught the wink and color of a dress parade at Fort Brady. He glanced idly at the Hudson Bay Post on the Canadian shore. And he wondered for the thousandth time how the Ojibway fishermen were able to hold their balance as they stood erect in their canoes in a swirlpool below the rapids and jabbed their long-poled nets at whitefish darting in the stream.

Meanwhile, Kate turned to the first page of *The Song Of Hiawatha,* and began to read:

> Should you ask me whence these stories?
> Whence these legends and traditions,
> With the odors of the forest,
> With the curling smoke of wigwams,
> With the rushing of great rivers?
> I should answer, I should tell you,
> From the great lakes of the Northland,
> From the land of the Ojibways.

Harvey, all ears, sat up straighter. He had a swift vision of Mr. Whittier offering him a huge slice of squash pie, and the words of the Quaker poet came back to him:

"To do justice to Schoolcraft's Ojibway legends of the Lake Superior Country would be a long task." Then, chuckling over his pun. "Perhaps I should say a *Long*fellow's task!"

Now, as Kate continued her reading, his ear caught the echo of familiar Upper Peninsula names — Escanaba, Tahquamenaw — and when Kate's clear voice reached the part in the poem where Hiawatha fought Pau-Puk-Keewis, and the cunning Storm Fool

> Sped away in gust and whirlwind,
> On the shores of Gitche Gumee,
> Westward by the Big-Sea-Water,
> Came unto the rocky headlands,
> To the Pictured Rocks of sandstone,
> Looking over lake and land scape —

Harvey grinned and shouted boyishly, "That's Lake Superior he's talking about!"

He had another swift vision of Mr. Whittier handing him William Cullen Bryant's eagle feather souvenir of his Lake Superior tour. Once again he recalled the quaint way of speaking the Quaker poet had, and his parting words:

"If thy travels ever take thee around Boston and Cambridge, call upon Professor Longfellow at Harvard, tell him about my pun on his name, and pass along the keepsake to him for inspiration. Who knows, my young friend? Many a truth has been spoken in jest, and great projects have depended on lesser trifles than an eagle's plume!"

Harvey shook his head in wonder at the part he had played in all this. He pictured twinkling blue eyes in a Santa Claus face at Cambridge, and he heard Harvard's great professor saying:

"A long task for a *Long*fellow, eh?" Then, after a broad
smile, a serious look. "The hand of fate may be in this.
By a strange coincidence, I am about to study Mr. Schoolcraft's books about the Indians, and now you bring me an
eagle plume for inspiration, and tell me that you are on
your way to the very place where the legends were collected
— "

Shaking his head at the miracle and mystery of it all,
young Charles Harvey watched the rainbows in the rapids.
Here, on Elmwood's lawn in the flow of Professor Longfellow's verses, he could hear the rise and fall and repeti-
tion of Ojibway music, of Lake Superior's pulse.

When Kate finished the last line, he wanted to know what
part of the poem she liked best.

She had no trouble turning to the proper page.

"Here it is," she said softly.

> When I think of my beloved,
> Ah me! think of my beloved,
> When my heart is thinking of him,
> O my sweetheart, my Algonquin!

Harvey supposed that kind of thing was all right for
girls, but, as for himself, the part that meant the most was
where Hiawatha and his friend Kwasind had tamed the
river:

> Cleared its bed of root and sand-bar,
> Dragged the dead trees from the channel,
> Made its passage safe and certain,
> Made a pathway for the people!

Kate smiled at him. "That's what you've done, Young
Mister Big," she said. "Made a pathway for the people
with your Soo Canal. See what a pair the two of you make?
Harvey and Hiawatha!"

Harvey, pleased at the comparison, scowled to cover his
pleasure — and fished for the compliment. "You don't have

to make fun of me," he growled, "just because I like a certain part of the poem."

Kate shook her curls. "I'm not making fun of you. I mean it."

Her eyes were busy, racing over the notes Professor Longfellow had written at the end of his poem.

"Listen!" she said in excitement. "Here's why the advance copy was sent to Elmwood! Listen to what he says:

'*The Song of Hiawatha* is founded on a tradition prevalent among the North American Indians, of a personage of miraculous birth, who was sent among them to clear their rivers, forests, and fishing grounds. He was known among different tribes as Hiawatha.

'Mr. Schoolcraft gives an account of Hiawatha in his works. Into this old tradition I have woven other curious Indian legends, drawn chiefly from the various and valuable writings of Mr. Schoolcraft, to whom the literary world is greatly indebted for his indefatigable zeal in rescuing from oblivion so much of the legendary lore of the Indians.

'The scene of the poem is among the Ojibways on the southern shore of Lake Superior, in the region between the Pictured Rocks and the Grand Sable.'

Kate raised raised shining eyes to Harvey. "There's the answer!" she cried. "Professor Longfellow sent an advance copy of his poem to Elmwood because this is where Mr. Schoolcraft wrote down the Indian legends. So, in a way, Elmwood is where Hiawatha was born, and a copy of the poem belongs here before it belongs anywhere else!"

Harvey objected mildly: "There's nothing on the package to say Professor Longfellow sent it."

Kate dismissed all argument. "Why should there be? It speaks for itself!" She turned to another of Professor Longfellow's notes.

"And listen to this: 'I pored over Mr. Schoolcraft's writings nearly three years.' Isn't that a marvelous coincidence? You started your canal and Professor Longfellow started his poem at the same time, just about!"

Harvey, letting her tell him what he already knew, and having fun raising objections, made another:

"Well, I came to the Soo and began to drum up a canal three years ago, but I didn't start actual construction until two years ago."

Kate sighed in exasperation. "Maybe Professor Longfellow didn't start *construction* on his *job* right away either, but he was thinking about it! The point is, you both began wonderful projects about three years ago and now you've both finished your two epics at practically the same time!"

Harvey grinned at her enthusiasm. "You make it sound as though we've been racing each other — my canal against his poem. There's not much comparison, you know," he added, to see her temper flare. "If you ask me, I think it ought to be a lot easier to build a poem than to build a canal!"

Kate stamped her foot and her cheeks glowed. "You!" she said. "Men! A great poem is just as important because it carries ideas!"

It amused Harvey to tease her. "But you've got to admit," he went on, "that the greatest poem in the world can't carry boats laden with iron and copper and wheat, which is what I'm interested in having carried!"

Kate gave him a flashing look and stormed up the Fort Brady Road, refusing to glance around when he called after her.

He didn't follow. He knew that, once her temper cooled down, Kate would realize he had only been teasing, and they would be good friends again, but there was no use trying to make up now.

Instead, he went inside Elmwood and put the small advance copy of Professor Longfellow's *Song of Hiawatha* beside the bulky volumes of Mr. Schoolcraft that were on the battered desk where so many of the Indian legends had been written — and where so many blueprints and reports and orders connected with the Soo Canal had been handled.

Then he wandered through the old house, reciting the lines that he would never forget, because they seemed to speak of him and his canal:

> Made its passage safe and certain,
> Made a pathway for the people!

27

Broken Bottleneck

The afternoon with Kate — her excited comments about the poem and the canal, and his good-natured teasing in return — had vividly brought back the day when young Charles Harvey had arrived at Sault Ste. Marie aboard a sidewheel steamer with four hundred workmen, mules and horses, tools and supplies, brought up from Detroit to start the digging of the big ditch.

In the morning, his mind was firmly, and finally, made up on the subject that was causing heated speculation along the Great Lakes, and violent discussion among boat crews who considered a black eye or a bloody nose the soundest kind of argument.

Knowing that his verdict was awaited with bated breath from Sachets Harbor at the toe of Lake Ontario to the head of navigation at the Soo, Harvey sent word from Canal Headquarters to Captain Jack Wilson of the sidewheeler *Illinois.*

"Just tell him I'd like to see him a minute," he said casually, but he placed a pitcherful of raspberry shrub and two glasses on the desk.

"A ceremony!" yelled John Tallman Whiting, with one glance at the desk, and he bolted for the waterfront to fetch Captain Wilson.

The whole Soo came jostling at their heels to crowd around the door and peek in the windows while Cap Wilson, with one side of his face clean-shaven and the other side still covered with lather, reported to Young Mister Big.

134

Harvey stood up and raised his glass in a wide-smiling toast.

"Captain," he thundered, "let's drink to the good ship *Illinois,* first to bring the canal gangs here to start the big ditch, and first — in a few days — to sail through the completed Soo Canal!"

Captain Wilson could hardly hold his glass for excitement, and the crowd outside, pleased by Harvey's fair decision, cheered and then roared as a little girl — the daughter of one of the captain's sailors — slipped through the legs of the men to skip her way into Wilson's arms, while he hugged her, forgetful of the lathered side of his face!

Harvey ordered the *Illinois* decked out with bunting and banners, dolled up for the Wedding of the Lakes.

Two days after Young Mister Big had celebrated his twenty-sixth birthday, Governor Bingham, in a tall-hatted ceremony alongside the locks, formally accepted the Soo Canal on behalf of his state in consideration of seven hundred and fifty thousand acres of timber and mineral lands in Michigan.

"In spite of cholera, sub-zero weather, malicious connivers, and the isolation of an outpost frozen away from civilization six months of the year, and other hardships and handicaps beyond our imagination," stated Governor Bingham handsomely, "this has been the most honorably performed contract ever entered into with a state or national government — "

Charles Harvey, the only young man on the speakers' stand, replied as General Agent of the St. Mary's Falls Ship Canal Company.

"No need making speeches," he said briefly. "If we've done a good job, the Soo Canal will do the talking for us!"

He faced toward Lake Superior and cupped his hands into a megaphone. "Gangway!" he shouted. "Gangway for tomorrow!"

Steamboat whistles blew and mission bells rang out the news that Charles Thompson Harvey, a traveling salesman for the Fairbanks Scales Company of St. Johnsbury, Vermont, a young man sent to Sault Ste. Marie for a rest cure, had promoted a canal on the roof of the world at the edge of nowhere and then gone on to build it in less than two years since breaking ground!

And what had he ever built before? Not so much as a picket fence! Not so much as a wooden sidewalk! Only a toy bridge in the backyard when he was a boy of twelve! And that, bragged the canal gangs, was all the practice Young Mister Big needed to build the world's mightiest mile!

The crowning event of the gala day came when Michigan's favorite sons, celebrities from every corner of the globe, thronged across the gangplank onto the deck of the *Illinois.*

There were bearded men of great fame who stared in wonder at the raw youth who had performed a miracle of construction. But young Charles Harvey was staring in awe at some of the bearded men!

Legend Maker Henry Rowe Schoolcraft was ill in Washington and had to send his regrets, but Iron Hunter Burt and Trail Blazer Cass were on deck.

Old Bill Burt who winked at Harvey in memory of days in Lansing, Judge Burt who had discovered every iron range in the Lake Superior jackpot, from Michigan's Gogebic and Menominee and Marquette to Minnesota's mighty Mesabi!

Seventy-year-old Senator Cass, Andy Jackson's onetime Secretary of War, who had explored and adventured across this wilderness of waterways in a paddle-and-portage birch-bark canoe with Schoolcraft.

In awe of such titans, young Harvey edged closer to Peter White, another up-and-coming young man who was well on his way toward making the region around Marquette known as Peter White's Country.

For those who had the Gift of Hearing, the Voices of the Rapids were singing a song of the future.

Baptiste Beaubien, his eyes on the *Illinois,* his ear cocked to mid-stream of the brawling St. Mary's River where a phantom brigade of canoes rode the wild waters, dipping their canoes endlessly, calling forever from behind a curtain of spray, Baptiste Beaubien listened to the song.

The old voyageur, proud in his wide red sash, his white head jaunty with a portage champion's red eagle feather, smiled in approval as the Mist People, the Huntsmen, sang the glory-to-come of a young man's canal.

Greater than the Panama, greater than the Suez, greater than the Panama and Suez Canals put together!

With a toot to be heard in the next century, the *Illinois,* 927 tons, Captain Jack Wilson, master, pulled away from the river dock below the rapids.

Sidewheels chunking the Irish-green water to foam, the steamer entered the Soo Canal and moved along America's Mightiest Mile.

A brawny blacksmith fired off an anvil cannon as the spot was passed where Harvey's Hammer had been forged.

Up on the texas deck, Captain Wilson shook a speaking trumpet at the cheering crowds lining the embankment and called:

"All aboard for Iron Bay, Copper Harbor, Isle Royale, Marquette, Duluth, North Star, and Setting Sun!"

Banners flying, a German band playing, the steamer pulled into the locks.

From his place on deck, young Charles Harvey gave the signal that released enough water into the locks to raise the *Illinois* to the level of Lake Superior.

Then the locks were opened and one of the greatest milestones in history was reached.

The sidewheeler had crossed a bridge of water from the Lower Lakes to the coldest, largest, richest lake on earth. Boosted through two locks, she had been stepped up a ladder of water, lifted eighteen feet, from bottom to top of the Falls of St. Mary's, to reach the level of Lake Superior.

The bottleneck of the Soo was broken. The Wedding of the Lakes was accomplished. The Inland Seas were joined, and the United States was assured of the highest place among all nations.

Perhaps only Senator Cass alone, the statesman who had missed being President by an eyelash, had a full vision of what June 18th, 1855 would mean to history. But all the others aboard the *Illinois* — even the mere flag-wavers and money-graggers — had an inkling of what the Soo Canal would accomplish.

Captain Jack Wilson, fully alive to the importance of the occasion and also aware of the importance of his passengers, took them on an excursion cruise across Lake Superior's Whitefish Bay and then along the south shore, past the places all sightseers wanted to view — the Pictured Rocks, and then, coming home, the Grand Sable where the Ojibways kept their deer meat fresh and unspoiled all summer in sandbank layers of prehistoric ice, unmelted for millions of years!

From the Pictured Rocks to the Grand Sable, Harvey stood on deck and watched the shoreline that was the scene of much of Professor Longfellow's *Song of Hiawatha*.

"Made its passage safe and certain," he recited half-aloud. *"Made a pathway for the people!"*

Senator Cass approached and stared at him strangely. "I beg your pardon, young man. Were you speaking to me?"

Harvey blushed in hot embarrassment. "No, sir," he replied. "I was just talking to myself. It would sound silly to anybody else."

Senator Cass raised his heavy eyebrows. "Let someone else be the judge of that." His voice cracked out with the habit of authority. "Speak up, boy!"

Harvey felt as if he were back in a Colchester, Connecticut, schoolroom. He stammered out the two lines of Professor Longfellow's poem, with an explanation of why they appealed to him. His eyes were downcast. He dared not look up from the boat deck, afraid of hearing the Senator's sudden gust of laughter.

Then, surprisingly, he felt an arm go around his broad shoulders as the white-haired man who once had been Governor of Michigan Territory said:

"I can't think of a better way to describe your Soo Canal, son — *a passage safe and certain, a pathway for the people.* That's what you've built, as time will tell!

28

Gangway for Tomorrow

The *Illinois* sidewheeled back to the Soo and docked at the head of the rapids where its important passengers hurried ashore to return to their important duties all over the United States.

Young Charles Harvey finished up his last duties at Canal Headquarters. The company dissolved. Its job was done.

As Harvey cleared up the paper work, he watched the bustling out the window.

He saw the steamer *Baltimore,* Captain John Reed, master, pass through the locks, bound eastward, the first boat ever to pass from Lake Superior into the Lower Lakes, down the eighteen-foot stepladder of the two locks and over the mile-long bridge paved with water.

He saw the brig *Freeman* become the first sailing vessel on the canal, bound up.

He recognized history in the making as the brigatine *Columbia* came winging out of Lake Superior to drop her sails while the locks took her down below the Falls of St. Mary's — the *Columbia,* Captain Judson Wells, master, with a hundred tons of Cleveland-Cliffs iron ore on her decks, the first real cargo from Lake Superior's mines, first in a series to turn the United States from a second-rate world power into the mightiest nation of all time.

The *Columbia!*

Finally he took a last look around Canal Headquarters, then turned the key in the lock and gave it to the custody of the canal's Michigan superintendent.

For the final time, he saddled the mouse-colored pony and rode out toward Fort Brady. It was a solemn occasion when he entered Elmwood where Hiawatha, in a manner of speaking, had been born — and where, also in a manner of speaking, the Soo Canal had been raised!

He sat for a precious moment at the battered desk, and, as he closed his eyes briefly, the room filled with phantoms of the past — a great chief, an Ojibway princess, an entire tribe standing in single file to collect their treaty payments from Henry Rowe Schoolcraft, a medicine man waiting to tell another legend of his people to the folklore historian destined to inspire Longfellow's greatest poem.

Charles Harvey took a lingering look at the huge School-craft volumes that dwarfed the small advance copy of *Hiawatha* sent from Cambridge to join them; and then, also for the last time, he closed another door behind him and walked away, leading the pony to a town stable.

He carried his bags up the steps of the Baptist Mission and knocked on the screen door.

When Kate Bingham came out on the porch to greet him, he said in an awkward voice: "I'm moving on, to find other things to do. I've come to say goodbye, Kate."

Her pretty face crumpled. "Oh, I see."

Harvey tore at his collar nervously. "You don't see at all," he told her. "I mean, I've come to say goodbye, unless, unless" — the words came tumbling out — "you'll marry me and go along!"

Kate made a radiant bride.

After the wedding the young couple boarded a steamer below the rapids, and then stood hand in hand at the rail as the ship was locked up through the Soo Canal, the real

Northwest Passage, the key to empire, the national pike to Manifest Destiny.

They were sailing toward the iron-throned, copper-crowned Queen of Lakes, the great sweetwater sea, the lake with the name that showed how far she surpassed all other lakes — Lake *Superior!*

"Sailing toward *our* future on *your* canal," Kate said softly, and added; "Young Mister Big!"

Charles Harvey smiled ahead.

The steamer blew for passage, and the lock gates opened wide — wide as tomorrow!

29

Shake Hands, Sir

Fifty years later, Charles Harvey returned to Sault Ste. Marie, by special invitation of the State of Michigan and the Federal government, to attend the Semi-centennial celebration of the completion of the Lake Superior Ship Canal.

He saw his name carved on a tall white marble monument in Canal Park. He was honored with the title of Grand Marshall, and he rode a stamping black horse in the Parade.

In the half century gone by, his canal — as Kate always called it — had developed the greatest concentration of marine tonnage in the world, and had become of such great value to the United States and to Canada, and indeed to all the world, that the Federal government had taken over its control.

Young Harvey's locks had been followed by the Weitzel and then by the Poe locks, but the Soo Canal, for all the changes made by modern progress, was still essentially what Harvey first had dreamed and then made into a reality — a pathway for the people.

During the Semi-centennial celebration on the second and third days of August, 1905, the people came, forty thousand of them from all over the world, to see the grand pageant. They heard the Vice President of the United States and the Solicitor General of Canada explain, along with other famous speakers, the significance of the occasion honoring a young man's canal.

Naval salutes at sunrise told British subjects and American citizens on each side of the St. Mary's River that the international celebration had begun. Humanity massed the sides of the huge Poe lock, cheering as a holiday fleet of ships bearing statesmen and celebrities moved upstream. Children played games, trying to guess the meaning of the masthead ensigns or vainly counting the banners that dressed the ships from stem to stern.

Sunshine threw rainbows in the rapids and danced upon the gold and brass of officers and their vessels. As the fleet turned and the lead ship passed through the Canadian locks, two Ojibway chiefs danced a war dance on her decks. The Canadian Soo went wild with cheers. Boat and factory whistles split the air. Dogs howled and children squealed with delight. Charles Harvey looked on, smiling, his eyes bright.

Gun salutes were fired as the fleet made a half-moon maneuver in the harbor. The cannons boomed out nineteen times for the Vice President and seventeen times for Michigan's governor.

With so much thunder and smoke of celebration, blood tingled, muscles tightened, lungs expanded — and the crowd shouted for more. It was a great day for the young in heart!

Two regimental bands were playing in the canal park at Old Fort Brady, and the world-famous Calumet & Hecla Mining Company Band seemed determined to drown both out with its brass and drums. Grand Marshall Harvey chuckled and listened with fond memories to the blare and beat of the Copper Country band.

Peter White of Marquette, President of the Semi-Centennial Celebration Commission, came up to where Harvey was sitting on the park bench and nodded at the gala band.

"Calumet & Hecla, greatest name in copper," he said. "Almost a thousand dollars a share, and still rising. That was one of your picks, Harvey, remember? There were some real bonanzas on those lands you picked out for the Canal Company. Did you know they expanded Cleveland-Cliffs, Michigan's greatest iron mine, on another of your selections?"

Harvey nodded. It seemed only yesterday since he had made out those land lists. But — fifty years! Where had the time gone?

"We've heard about you," Peter White said. "There was that railroad you promoted from Lake Superior clear down to the Gulf of Mexico. Too bad it was sidetracked by the Civil War. Then we read the headlines about you building the first elevated railroad in New York City, first in the world, I guess. And now you're one of the advisors on which canal route we ought to take down there in Panama or Nicaragua, aren't you?"

Harvey nodded again, busy with thoughts of the past.

Peter White stroked his beard, a gesture he had acquired since becoming a mining tycoon and a Regent of the University of Michigan. "This neck of the woods is just as proud of you as those people in New York who claim you've done more for the comfort of its inhabitants with your rapid transit 'El' than anyone else who ever walked the city's streets.

"We're so proud of you," Peter White went on, "that we named a Marquette iron mine after you — the Charles T. Harvey — and not a bad producer either. But I don't have to tell you anything about mining. You organized the Pioneer Iron Smelting Company only two years after you finished the Soo Canal."

Peter White wagged a finger under Harvey's nose in mock reproach. "Trouble with you is, you couldn't stay put in one place any longer than a Mexican jumping bean. You hopped from Marquette over to Manistique to build a dam, and you cleared the entrance of the Ontonagon River so ships could sail through the channel and pick up cargoes of copper. Then you engineered and built the first mail and stage road to Lake Superior from the south, at Green Bay."

Harvey's eyes flashed with youthful fire as the memory carried him back to the adventurous days of his early manhood. "Mexican jumping bean, am I?" he echoed. "This is a big country, and it keeps a man hopping if he wants to go places. I've paddled and portaged my way up wilderness streams from the Two Heart to the Tobacco River."

He smiled at a joke on himself "Once I traveled up a Wisconsin tree to put safe distance between me and a she-bear with cubs. I've been shipwrecked and had to take to a raft during a storm on Lake Superior. One time my horse sank under me in a Minnesota swamp and I had to dismount and lead a search party back to haul him out of the bog. Another time I was crossing an arm of Lake Michigan in a two-horse sleigh when crash! we went through the ice, and I barely managed to save the team and myself, but my clothes were frozen so stiff that they rattled in the wind!"

"I remember," said Peter White. "That was the first stage of your journey to Washington where you were headed to promote land grants for the Milwaukee & St. Paul and the Chicago & Fond du Lac Railroads, now called the Chicago & Northwestern."

"In those days we called everything the Soo Line," Harvey smiled. "And you should have seen the people's faces when I landed in the nation's capital, with my snowshoes strapped to my grip. A whole crowd followed me right into the hotel lobby, staring their eyes out."

"Crowds have a habit of following you, and staring," Peter White said soberly. "The trouble with the way you started out here at the Soo," he continued with a chuckle, "is that you've done some mighty big things since, but there's no chance of you or any other man beating your first performance — the Soo Canal! When you left here, your future was all behind you!" Peter White chuckled deeper. "But that's why this afternoon's parade is going to march *behind* you — because you're the man who built the canal we're celebrating!"

True enough, in the afternoon, Grand Marshall Harvey rode at the head of the parade on a prancing jet-black horse. Michigan's favorite sons and all the world celebrities, including the Vice President of the United States, came trailing behind on their mounts or in carriages.

Harvey, honored above all, rode up the street where once he had seen the snaking tracks of a portage raiload.

Now there was a trolley line!

He passed street fairs — shooting galleries, cane-racks, toy balloon and doll displays, sandwich stands, and Indian souvenir vendors — where once Ojibway tepees and fur trading posts had stood. Riding along under the flags and banners and bunting that lined the thoroughfares, he remembered leading the canal gangs to church when the road was little more than two wagon ruts.

Once, as he pranced by, he heard a little boy in the crowd ask: "Who's the old man with the white beard, Momma?"

"Hush!" the mother replied. "You mustn't call him an old man, darling, he's a distinguished gentleman."

Another time, and it was the high spot of the parade for Harvey, he saw a wrinkled, bald fellow hurl his cane in the air and yell: "Hooraw for Young Mister Big!"

The tribute from a onetime member of his canal gangs meant more than all the compliments paid Harvey by officials and statesmen in the speeches made during the entire two-day celebration.

Each evening there were fireworks, and more fireworks, to delight the youngsters, and the grownups like Harvey who had never become old in spirit. The Canadians stole the fireworks show. The likeness of King Edward and the reproduction of Niagara Falls, done in gold and blue and red fire, and extending across several hundred feet of Canadian waterfront, brought the American crowds to their feet with awed gasps and whistles.

Harvey, staring at the pinwheels and rockets, thought of the night when the steam punch had been buried in the roaring ruins of the blacksmith shop on the canal cut.

The last day of the celebration, he sat in a place of honor on the speakers' stand, his ears ringing hour after hour with high praise of the great ditch he had dug and the mighty mile he had paved with water a full half century in the past.

He stroked his white beard and smoothed back his white hair. It was hard for him to believe that he was seventy-six, older than Judge Burt, older even than Senator Cass had been, when they had sat with him on the speakers' stand the day the side-wheeler *Illinois* had made its historic passage through the brand-new Soo Canal.

Harvey glanced out over the rapids where the Mist People, the old voyageur's Huntsmen, still sang, as they had sung fifty years ago, as they would sing fifty years from now, as they would keep on singing forever.

He dozed a little in his chair. Talk, talk, talk.

Harvey remembered what he had said a long time ago on a speakers' stand not far from this same spot: "No need making speeches. If we've done a good job, the Soo Canal will do the talking for us!"

With the playing of *America* by the First United States Infantry band, the Semi-Centennial Celebration came to an official close.

Harvey stayed in his seat, staring out at the canal, while the crowds filed from the stands. A boy of about twelve came up to him and said, a bit bashfully: "I'm doing this on a kind of dare, but my family got its start working for you, Mr. Harvey, and I figured you might do it."

Harvey smiled. "Your father worked on the canal?"
The boy shook his head. "Oh, no, sir, my grandfather!"
Harvey, reminded of age again, grunted. "I see. Well,
what do you want me to do for you, son?"

The boy rubbed a nervous palm across the seat of his
pants. "Shake hands with me, sir, if you please."

Harvey stared in astonishment. "Is that all?" He
pumped the boy's hand up and down in fine style. "Are you
sure you don't want anything else, son?"

The boy grinned. "That's plenty, sir! From now on, if
anybody ever shakes hands with me, I can always let them
know that they're shaking the hand that shook the hand of
the man who built the Soo Canal!"

Harvey laughed as the boy scurried away, probably to
collect a penny bet for doing the dare, and then he watched
from the solitary speakers' stand while sunset painted the
moving mile of water.

He had built it as a young man. That was why, at
seventy-six he could not imagine himself as old.

As long as there was a Soo Canal, he would always be a
young man at heart.

He took one last look before he turned away.

There would always be a Soo Canal!

The St. Mary's Rapids were not saying goodbye. They
were calling: "So long, Young Mister Big!"

30

Eagles in Their Eyes

When Michigan and the nation made preparations to celebrate the one hundredth birthday of the Soo Canal, in the centennial year 1955, the name of Charles Thompson Harvey was not on the invitation list.

The former Grand Marshall, the honored guest at the speakers' stand, the man responsible for the entire celebration, would have to be present in spirit.

But, although his voice was silenced, his canal was still speaking for him, and louder than ever!

Up on the roof of the world, locked in ice and idle all winter, the canal built by Young Mister Big was carrying more water-born tonnage than the great Panama and Suez Canals combined, despite the fact that the latter were open to traffic the year round.

The hard-working Cinderella of its kind, short on publicity but long on results, the Soo Canal gradually earned credit as the most important commercial canal in the world. Where Charles Harvey once saw ships hauled and tugged up Water Street around the rapids, now sails the largest freshwater fleet on the globe.

In World War Two, Michigan's Mighty Mile became recognized as the most precious mile in the United States, indeed in the entire Western Hemisphere. Young Mister Big's canal was the bridge that connected Lake Superior's iron ranges with Pittsburgh, Chicago, Cleveland, and Detroit — to produce the guns and shells and armor plates and other weapons that defeated the Axis powers.

With the atomic era at hand, the Soo gained additional importance as men — young as Harvey had been, and old as Judge Burt — hurried through the canal with their Geiger counters to explore the Lake Superior wilderness for uranium deposits.

Rich strikes were made, richer and more vital perhaps than the bonanza yieldings of Calumet & Hecla copper or Cleveland-Cliffs iron, richer than all the iron in the Marquette, Menominee, Gogebic, Mesaba, and Vermilion ranges, stretching across Michigan and Wisconsin and Minnesota and into Canada.   ,

Visitors no longer were permitted too close to the canal.

The armed forces never went so far as to post Harvey's original warning: TRESPASSERS SHOT ON SIGHT — *And Prosecuted Next Summer if Alive,* but great care against sabatage had to be taken of this national asset more valuable than all the gold buried at Fort Knox.

Today, the Cinderella Canal that has the honor of being the greatest link in the St. Lawrence Seaway under construction, also is being fitted for her glass slipper — the longest and costliest bridge in the world. Spanning the Straits of Mackinac to connect the Soo Canal and Lake Superior's resources by highway to Michigan's Lower Peninsula and the motor-minded United States, this bridge marks the accomplishments of boyhood dreams — the dreams of boys like Charles Harvey, who started out by building a backyard bridge in Colchester, Connecticut, and was forbidden any helping of blueberry pie for supper, because he came late to the table.

Old Fort Brady is little more than a memory along the St. Mary's River, but Camp Lewis guards the heights overlooking the canal, and at nearby Kinross Airbase, jet planes keep constant vigil.

The young men who fly these planes have eagles in their eyes, the *Gunfighter Look* that twenty-three-year-old

Charles Harvey had when he first arrived at Sault Ste. Marie.

In the more than a hundred years since then, the Soo has known many changes. At the Semi-Centennial Celebration, visitors saw that the original Harvey locks had been replaced by the Weitzel and the Poe. Visitors to the Centennial Exposition saw two more locks, the Davis and the Sabin, as well as the newest and deepest of all the locks, the MacArthur, geared to the St. Lawrence Seaway and Saltwater vessels.

Young Mister Big's canal has become the Miracle Mile that changed the United States from a second-rate power to Number One among the nations. Known as the Billion Dollar Mile, and America's Mightiest Mile, it is a leader in peace and in war. Because of what it has done and what it is capable of doing, the Soo Canal is at the top of any enemy target list.

But the country that produced Charles Harvey is also producing the jet pilots with the eagles in their eyes.

All boys are born hero-worshippers. Perhaps the pilots fly the way they do, with no thought of fear or failure, because of the story that has been handed down from generation to generation at the Soo — the story about the young traveling salesman who came north for a rest-cure, and, because he didn't know when he was beaten, went slam-bang against all opposition and built the Soo Canal!

Young Mister Big blazed the trail. The young men with eagles in their eyes intend to keep it what he made it — a pathway for the people, the free people of this world!

W. R.

The Dockside Press
Shipyard Row, Charlevoix, Michigan
Couse's Landing, Palm Beach, Florida